C000090704

Stretto

David Wheatley was born in Dublin and is the author of five collections of poetry, most recently *The President of Planet Earth* (Carcanet). His other publications include a critical study, *Contemporary British Poetry* (Palgrave), and, as co-editor with Ailbhe Darcy, *The Cambridge History of Irish Women's Poetry*. He has written for *London Review of Books*, *Times Literary Supplement*, *The Guardian*, *Literary Review* and *Poetry Review*. He lives with his family in rural Aberdeenshire. *Stretto* is his first novel.

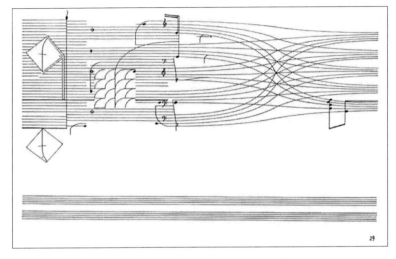

29

from Cornelius Cardew, *Treatise* (1967)

DAVID WHEATLEY

Stretto

 editions

First published in 2022
by CB editions
146 Percy Road London W12 9QL
www.cbeditions.com

Frontispiece: Cornelius Cardew: *Treatise*
Edition Peters No. 7560
© 1967 by Gallery Upstairs Press, USA.
© 1970 assigned to Peters Edition Limited, London.
Reproduced by permission of the Publishers.

Printed in England by Blissetts, Brentford, TW8 9EX

ISBN 978–1–909585–46–1

For Alec Finlay

§ 1

The more difficult it becomes to deny the failure of my years abroad, the more my thoughts return to the memory of a mountain village on a reservoir in the region of my youth. I say 'my long years abroad', though I write from there now and hardly think of it as abroad anymore; it is simply where I happen to be. But this too is a part of my failure, for reasons that will become apparent. A phrase such as 'the failure of my years abroad' sounds melodramatic, and in returning to my childhood I may give the sense that it holds the key to that failure. Not so. But their connection is nevertheless real, unlikely though this may appear. The village lies in the western portion of the mountain range that defined my early years, on an artificially created reservoir. The village is approached on more than one side by a causeway, and lies on a strip of land that, it too, is narrow and elongated, lending itself to the spread-out pattern of roadside dwellings common in that part of the world. Arriving early by bicycle one morning, I notice a parish church built in a style I recognise as deriving from the southern United States. Later I would learn that local stonemasons had travelled to New Mexico, where their skills were much in demand, and on their return home had brought that state's distinctive church architecture with them. Though not religious, I rarely passed a church in those days without looking inside, make of this what you will. Imagine my surprise then to find a series of stained-glass windows therein by a well-known early twentieth-century artist. Of the two panels, perhaps the more striking is the one depicting the Virgin Mary. The upper half of her body gives way to a series of jewels in a manner I associate with the cover of a medieval psaltery, though all the more brilliant in this case for their frame of black. I sit for a time in contemplation, noting the lack of similarity between this Virgin Mary and her more formulaic representations. I have stated that I am not religious, but find my response to the window crystallising into a stand-off between light and dark. It is a dull autumn day, and amid so much encircling gloom I have discovered a window of light. It seems crucially important, therefore, and for this moment at least possible, that I pass through the window to whatever lies beyond. And so I do, imaginatively at least. The effects of this resolution have continued to unfold down well beyond that moment, while also leading me to the failure recorded in my opening sentence. How this came about will form the burden of the notes that follow.

§ 2

As I write these words, I turn my left hand over and study the
lines of scar tissue on the edge of my palm where I put my
hand through a window as a boy. We had returned home from
an outing, and I bounded up the path before slamming into
the window. The glass was frosted, but behind it I remember
a light that must have been left on in our absence. I do not
recall the aftermath of my accident, painful though it must
have been. Ever since then I have thought of windows as sites
of opportunity but danger too. Years later, I am reading a volume on rhetorical tropes and encounter one called, I believe,
metalepsis. It involves the passage from one narrative frame to
another, as when a film begins with a page from a book, showing the words spoken by the narrator, with an illustration of for
instance a house or some skaters on a lake, before the illustration comes to life and we enter into its world. This convention
is normally used sparingly, but I have found myself drawn to
works of art where this becomes the norm. We become habit-
uated to one narrative world only for it to be yanked away,
as we pass through the window, and then the whole process
repeats itself, and we realise that the book is transition and
only transition, not the merely standing still, the merely being
there. But I am getting ahead of myself. Around the time I
was studying these rhetorical tropes, I had become aware of
another installation by the stained-glass artist, in a museum
in the city where I was a student. It is a series of windows
responding to the work of a famous Romantic poet who had
died young. The setting is desolate and wintry. A young man
has come to a castle on a surreptitious visit to his lover, with

whom he will elope. It is the eve of St Agnes, and the woman believes she will receive a dream vision of her future husband. The fantastical atmosphere makes dream and reality hard to tell apart, and the stained-glass installation reaches its apogee of narcotising intrigue when it shows the young woman lying beautifully asleep under a stained-glass window, which is to say a window within a window. The artwork has a room to itself in the gallery, and the feeling (by now familiar to me, indeed a sensation constantly on my mind) of passing into an imaginative dreamworld never fails to work its gaudy magic. With the window within the window, however, this effect is doubled to a state of exquisite intensity. The lovers are united and ride away together unnoticed. At the death, the poem jolts us back to workaday reality with an image of its ancient beadsman who 'after thousand aves told / For aye unsought for slept among his ashes cold', words I carry with me back onto the brisk streets of the capital outside. Here is a peculiar conflict. Does the window within the window add an extra layer of protection, sheltering us further and deeper inside its vision? Or did it make the return to the reality outside the artwork all the more painful when it comes, as it inevitably must? 'For aye unsought for slept among his ashes cold': I speak the line again, and am again that young man wavering undecided on that brink.

§ 3

All over the city where I study, the populace finds its own portals
into concealed realities, every few yards or so, or so it seems, in
the form of pub doors. Though not much of an drinker at this
time, I am familiar with a poster to be seen in city pubs of the
famous writers of my homeland, all men, and many with repu-
tations as legendary drinkers at this or that local establishment.
Yet my own fancy, I find, is taken by a writer not on this poster
– another nineteenth-century poet, who lived and died in the
city without ever (hardly) leaving it, but succeeded in leaving
almost no physical trace of his existence. Making a pilgrimage
to his birthplace, I find it bisected by a busy modern road, while
on a later visit I find the plaque on the wall marking his birth
has vanished. His enormous output is almost entirely lacking
in anything resembling topographical descriptions of the city.
This seems strangely at odds – for an alcoholic poet, as he was
– with the male-bonding and love of the local that defines the
culture of drinking. He did compose an essay, in 1832, describing a trip to a pub called The Shades, which no longer exists, in
which any prospect of bibulous camaraderie misfires. Observing a fellow drinker from a distance, he begins to speculate
feverishly as to his identity, believing him to be a necromancer.
He fantasises that the drinker's nose is growing, threatening to
cover 'every square of vacant space in the vacant metropolis.'
He then passes out and awakens at home in bed with a doctor
in attendance. The essay describes an anti-portal, or inside-out
portal, throwing the poet back on himself in a world where
even a banal drinking session with a crony defies all realist representation. In subsequent years I would come to spend more

time in pubs, but not (or not only) on account of any increased taste for alcoholic revelry. Rather, I desired to clear the hurdle that so defeated my nineteenth-century poet, which is to say everyday life at ease on arse and elbow on a barstool of the kind I too, as a young man, found so difficult to experience and represent. The transformative powers of the pub are less about drinking than access to a new physical realm, a space of light and dark, as when a glass of beer is raised to a gas-lamp in a windowless back room, and held aloft momentarily before consumption. Quaint image. But I am getting ahead of myself again. My nineteenth-century poet was also an opium addict and died at the tail-end of the Irish famine. An idealised bust of him stands in a city-centre park, with an inset of 'Dark Rosaleen', an idealised female embodiment of my homeland. The poet's nationalist admirers saw this image as a solution to the social dissonance and maladjustment I have described. Accepting this solution comes at the cost of a certain sublima-tion of the real problem, particularly where actual women are concerned, who after all are human too, whatever my home-land might have thought at the time. Nation as all-healing mother substitute. No. Fail. I linger briefly with my poet in The Shades but suggest we move on elsewhere for our next drink, through the portal again. But is this real, we ask each other simultaneously. Is this happening.

§ 4

The pauses at the stations remind me of the silences between tracks on my favourite albums. The pause of recent departure, the pause amidst resolute progress, the pause of last-minute hesitation before arrival. Were I to close my eyes and lose all sense of time, I would feel a pause and know it meant this or that station. I sit in the corner of the carriage, the right-hand side for preference, where I will have a view of the bay. The seat is not my seat, though I think of it as mine. People fill up the carriage under the unspoken rules of first one person per two facing seats; then two, once all facing seats have at least one occupant; then three, and so on to completion. Travellers entering at one end of the carriage will walk long distances to uphold these rules, sometimes even passing from carriage to carriage to do so. On the return trip later I will board the train from a different station from the one where I alight in the morning, for a higher chance of being reunited with my seat, since mine is the journey taken by the man in the corner of the carriage; otherwise it is no longer 'my' journey. Later the lay-out of the carriages changes, and my connection with the journey alters. This coincides with my moving away, which helps to formalise the disconnection. As we approach the city, to return to my morning journey, I look to the left and see as I do every day a white oval mirror in an upstairs window. It is inclined at an angle of maybe twenty degrees. In all my years of observing it I never succeed in spotting anyone looking into it, checking their hair or make-up before slipping out to work. The house is off down one of the narrow, cobbled streets near the canal. I cannot imagine the occupant walking a few hundred yards to work, since the city is built for no one's convenience; instead they must set off on an arduous trek to an industrial estate out west, or take the train south and swap journeys with me. Then another stop is added to the line at just this spot, another pause inserted into the continuum of the journey in and out. In the evening I walk the short distance across the river, with the algal, elephant legs of the railway bridge to my right, to secure a seat on the train home. As in the morning, my journey depends for reasons I do not grasp on the placing of my foot in the corner of the carriage when I sit down. But the train has yet to enter the station, and when it does travellers jostle, hoping to find themselves by a carriage door when it stops. I place a finger on the button as the train slides to a halt, and walk like this down the platform. My fellow commuters step back, deferring to my small preposterous piece of showmanship. The doors open on an empty carriage and, wedging my foot in the corner, I begin to pedal my way through a silent Bach fugue, an old favourite, subject and countersubject fitting together as we go like railway track and wheel.

§ 5

The face. Rip it off. What lurks beneath. I feel something brewing, subcutaneous. Long years begin of adipose congestion, of slow-rising spots. Lock that bathroom door if you please. Pop! A queasy undergraduate squeezing his pimples, Woolf called *Ulysses*. Look me in the – splat! – right in the eye. The inside is the outside. The taut little bubble isolated under two quick-working fingernails and voilà. The eye cannot see the eye. I look at the eye but can't see the eye seeing the eye. In a Magritte painting we see the back of a head staring into a mirror showing the back of a head. Twitch of the rods and cones as I gaze. Rod for the low-light levels and cones for the high. All my life I have struggled with a very specific band of blue and purple, what can this mean. The cones control colour vision and high spatial acuity. Pull in closer minus glasses I used to, to the point where near becomes blur and so less, less seen. Today I might photograph and blow up the image. A character in Borges fancied constellations were tracing their shapes in the marks on his face. Spelling their messages in crypto-alphabets. The endless baths to steam them out. When younger, with my terrible teeth I would cover my mouth with a hand while talking. Now there is a beard and long hair and a hat. Where is my face. But others' faces too recede. Prosopagnosia is the inability to recognise faces. In extreme cases this can progress to Capgras syndrome, a staple of fantasy-horror, as when a character believes their family members have been replaced by imposters, replicants. The only way to prove it is to rip off their masks and expose what lies beneath, be it something or nothing. Dreyer's silent film *La passion de Jeanne d'Arc*

9

is unusual in its focus on the characters' faces. For much of the film we see Joan's face in anguished close-up. Unusually, Renée Falconetti wore no make-up. Shots often focus and linger on facial imperfections, warts and moles. In constructing the set, Dreyer drew on medieval sources including Mandeville's *Livre des merveilles*, despite the fictive aspect of that text. He built an expensive replica castle only for it feature hardly at all in the film. There are only faces, there is only the face. Also featuring as the Dean of Rouen is Antonin Artaud, before his mental collapse and the terrible hollowing-out of his face. Later he would turn up on Aran bearing what he believed was the staff of St Patrick, before being deported from the country, leaving a trail of unpaid guest-house bills. But look for the moment at those faces. That face. The flames will devour it, transporting Joan to a beyond she never doubts, to the point of helping her executioners tie her bonds. Long presumed lost, a print of the final uncensored cut of the film was found in 1981 in an Oslo psychiatric hospital. Falconetti never acted again.

§ 6

'i am examining / my love for this child // who looks so like me / i am inside / his movements' (Tom Raworth). I am child-less and to understand succession must see myself as an infant from my parents' perspective. In truth my sense of longer historical perspectives is sketchy. Dipping into a local history book the first sentence I read is: 'The mountain range that frames the town was formed 400 million years ago by a mass of sedimentary rock pushing upwards in the earth's crust', and that's good, I like that. But to speak of more immediate lineage, my father was hanged by the militia in the village square in 1798 but distinguished himself in action in the General Post Office in 1916, namesakes of his I mean, though doubtless related, there being few enough of our tribe in these parts. Am I so quick to foresake this patrimony, I ask msyelf. Yes. Is my maternal grandmother's surname Jewish. Apparently not. It will later reveal itself as a common surname in the final country I move to, providing a readymade narrative of voyage and unexpected return. Do you feel very Scottish, mother. No. Though a well-known Red Clydeside MP appears to have been a great-great-uncle. They would have come and gone on the boats, back then, for the seasonal work. Known as an English experimental poet, Tom Raworth had an Irish passport but rarely features in discussions of Irish poetry. Perhaps the assumption is that, first-generation emigrant though he was, a certain cultural fade had occurred, a lack of intimacy with who the minister for transport might be or who might win the Leinster final. His more excitable, let's say, style of writing has also failed to find favour, in some quarters. That must have been the American influence, since it can't be from here. A puzzling and tenacious narrative. But down with this sort of thing. The bourgeois makes a world in their image and expects us to live in it, and this is the world we must destroy. Travelling to a school in the west of the capital city I watch the visiting Sorley MacLean read his work, entering a kind of vatic hallucinatory state as he does so. An angry poem addressed to Christ asks whether he has seen the downtrodden highland woman, *''S a' mhias chreadha trom air cùl'*, the clay basin heavy on her back, as the black sludge of her time descends into the peace of the grave. Another poem keeps up the heroic mood, conjuring *'an léine a bh'air O Conghaile'*, the shirt that was on Connolly's back when he was shot. Later I will hear the tale of how in a post-pub stupor MacLean nodded off on a sofa and repeatedly jolted himself awake with the phrase 'Who is the g-g-g-greatest of the Gaels'. But what are his thoughts on the by-election recount, or the provision of bus lanes on Stephen's Green, is that not Ireland too. Ask not the noble dreamer to stoop to such frippery. But now as I make these notes I too, I find, speak across a hallucinated distance, a zone of unlikeness where the niceties of a bourgeois world have come unstuck. I read them back by the light of a bedside lamp to the disbelief of the teenager I once was. Who is the minister for transport. G'wan Kilkenny. 'Say hello to my people.'

§ 7

Looking out over the roofs from the bathroom window of the music academy, I find I can see all the way down to the docks, their distant cranes and masts. Looking down from the room where I play the piano I see the pub on the corner and the old orange double-decker buses pass by, like great beasts of burden sloping to and from their watering holes. I walk the short distance daily from my room in the city to practise, and even now feel forming under my fingers the endless labyrinths of Bach's preludes and fugues. C major tonic chord becomes third-inversion secondary seventh becomes first-inversion dominant seventh. It is a grand piano and sometimes I will stand and explore the green-felted hammers and twang away on the strings as though I were playing the harp, just to get that much closer to the sound at source. A traffic light changes and on go the buses' brakes and I above them hear a D, the note itself, and turn to the prelude and fugue in that key, attuning myself to the world of the bus, entering the sound-world of my perfect pitch, perhaps the one natural talent I possess. For me, to mention Bach's preludes and fugues is already to hear them, to feel them unroll under my fingers, tapped out on a table-top or wherever. An important aspect of these pieces is the system of tuning celebrated in their title (*The Well-Tempered Clavier*). There are twelve notes in the chromatic scale, but not all keys were equally playable on eighteenth-century keyboards. Some were perfect-tuned, resulting in others being unplayable. Attempts to solve this problem often had an impractical aspect, as when black notes on keyboards were split down the middle to reflect E flat and D sharp being different notes, rather than 'enharmonic' twins. Apologies for the technical language. This is also why there are so many Scarlatti sonatas in G and E but rather fewer in A flat or D sharp. Tempered tuning was like a political union of keys where each traded a degree of sovereignty in return for the harmonious larger unit they would form. And which Bach decided to celebrate by writing a set of preludes and fugues in all twenty-four keys, major and minor. Bach had strong views about tuning, apparently, and would tune his major thirds a tad sharp. Legend also has it that the elaborate curlicues on the title page of the original *Well-Tempered Clavier* contain coded messages on this subject. But back to the perfect pitch. The bus brakes and I hear a note: D. I play a perfect fifth: D – A: and then another: E flat – B flat. But they are not the same interval; I hear tiny, millimetre shades of difference. If you are a singer and a song is too low, you hitch it up a tone or two. But the thought of changing the key of any of Bach's preludes and fugues seems little short of blasphemous. I cannot think of another piece of music with such an intimate relationship not just to the intervals that make up the piece but the actual notes themselves. The experience of hearing all the preludes and fugues in sequence is like nothing else I know. It is like circumnavigating the globe. By the time you reach the end, there are no notes left, no possibility of there being any left. Another bus brakes. This time an F. Play the prelude and fugue in F. The random prompts continue, and the Bach soundtrack I provide. Follow where it leads. Follow it to this day. Perhaps it is less the sounds of everyday life that summon the Bach preludes and fugues than the preludes and fugues that summon and create the sounds of everyday life, the sensation you feel of running one back tooth over another, tracing the distance between C and C sharp like a rusty door that squeaks on its hinges.

§ 8

Yet even as I travel the soundworld of a Bach prelude or fugue I double back, find windows opening within windows. Stretto is a fugue technique where the melody – the subject – is repeated in another voice, but before the statement of the original subject has finished. In the C major fugue from book one of the *Preludes and Fugues*, the subject is stated, then restated at shortening intervals, reducing from six beats to two and then one. In the C minor fugue in book two the closing use of stretto comes on like a motorway pile-up, with the crotchet version of the subject rapped out against the same thing in quavers. Apologies again for the technical language, we'll get past it soon. I give you the C minor fugue, as played by the person I spent my twenties wanting to be, Glenn Gould, as replayed by me. Gould's performances are highly idiosyncratic, involving the pianist humming along and displaying a wilfulness with tempi some would describe as childish, or even mad. All his life he sat on the same chair while playing, and when its seat fell out would perch on the edge, preferring not to have it restored. I wonder though whether stretto technique is remotely reproducible I wonder though whether stretto technique is remotely reproducible in verbal in verbal form form without it without it seeming seeming contrived or merely contrived impossible or merely impossible. Steady on. There is a Paul Celan poem called 'Engführung', which means stretto in German, and which doesn't appear to be about Bach, and is therefore probably all about Bach, the line of a Bach fugue circling back, compressing, expanding, speeding up, slowing down. And having played my Bach fugues at the academy I walk by the river, in an area soon to be redeveloped but for the moment still semi-derelict. Tied up by a yellow dockside crane is a Guinness boat, the *Miranda Guinness*, or the *Lady Patricia*, if not one the other, working the Irish sea route to transport stout to the drinkers on the neighbouring island. I imagine it sloshing around, a lough of the stuff, in the hold, by the bilge water, but sense this would not be practical. A friend is employed as a nightwatchman in the hut by the bollards, with the hawsers gathered and coiled on the cobbles outside. People come up and say the strangest things. Can I take it for an auld spin. Slip the guyropes and away. Has been done. Bumped into the bridge once. What, my friend did? No! We stand on the bridge amid an organ console of levers and knobs with outside the volleys of vigilant gulls and the spew of the sewer at low-tide while sightless tributaries pour into the tide. Off in the middle distance the Ormond Hotel's slow cool dim seagreen slides into shadow where echoes play in spangles under the feet on the bridge. Music of what happens. On which to play these small countersubjects, last echoes catching up with themselves before rushing on and dissolving into the bay. As part of his duties my friend is required to log all events, including non-events. On the hour he presses a button on his walkie-talkie, which squawks to life like an over-excited lapwing. 'Nothing', he intones, 'Nothing. Nothing.'

§ 9

The scratch of Spanish summer heat on the back of the neck.
Zurbarán's St Diego of Alcala carrying his cross. Pastel-bright
cherubs' heads floating in the ether of a counterreformation
baroque. Ideally a trip to the gallery occurs in the low light
of autumn, with this Spanish weather bursting over me like a
sensory assault as I step in from the rain. There is no one correct way to walk through a gallery. Choose a single picture and
enter its frame. Irish impressionist Frank O'Meara worked in
France and died young of malaria, in Carlow. In *Towards Night
and Winter* a lone female figure shakes out grain from a sheet
or apron against a line of gable-ends in the background. When
O'Meara took leave of Fanny Osbourne in 1878 he presented
her with a portrait of him by John Singer Sargent, sensing he
would never see her again. My attempts to recapture his colour
palette now, his Irish muting of that rich French light, come to
grief on the wildly different shadings of the reproductions of
the canvas I find online. Add to which the screen settings of
my computer, which I am hazy about at the best of times, and
which I find liable to sudden alteration by a flailing toddler's
foot, here and now, in the now I write in. I set *Towards Night
and Winter* as my screen-saver and circle it warily, approaching
now from the zero-at-the-bone of our near-arctic winter, now
from the fuller sun of our summer, fuller though northern than
the painting's French crepuscular season and moment. The
woman's hand opens and closes and scatters the grain over the
field for some geese who will remain forever just out of view.
Is there something you notice about this picture, the gallery
attendant asks, as I mope around aimlessly. After a pause she

points out that the paintings on the wall of the domestic interior are the same paintings on the wall of the gallery to my left and right. How did they manage that, I wonder. But do I remember or dream this, I ask myself now. Because if remembered, why have I never found that painting again. On later returns, though, I find whole wings of the gallery closed for years on end. Among my fondest memories of the place are the Turner watercolours bequeathed on condition that they be displayed only in January, when the light is at its weakest, both for the protection of the artworks and to create a light-world for them closest in spirit to their own. I cross the street from the college and indulge in my daily swill of newsprint in a café first before wiping my eyes clean in the gallery, peering at the watercolours past the face in the glass, my own, that pursues me so relentlessly. The watercolour is the most delicate of forms yet the most indelible too. It cannot be revised, no sooner is a brushstroke or a raindrop applied to the canvas than it is immutable. A temptation to hunch over the tiny artworks and sit among them staring into space till they put me out in the rain at closing time. So I do. Yet strangely of the 'indelible' watercolours themselves I recall not a thing.

§ 10

I am lying in the bath, pruning nicely and slipping occasionally below the water. In a Jean-Luc Godard film an audience watches a woman take a bath on screen and, beguiled by what they see, stand up for a better view. They rush the screen and tear it down, revealing behind it a woman in a bath. But what lurks behind this woman. Is it what lies behind the image we want or the image itself. As I slide under the water I watch a quizzical trail of bubbles ascend, like the unedited bubbles and blots one used to see before the opening credits at the cinema. Drawing stick men as a boy on the corner of my copy-books, then flipping them into motion, I directed my own small cinematic features. In the zoetrope, images circulate on a cylinder, and are watched through slits in the side. If not viewed through the slits the images blur together incoherently. Is it me, I wonder, spinning the zoetrope, who moves through the images, or is it they who move through me, the fixed point of my eye. Spin, spin. And stop. Or do we both move, and if so, in synch or not. Flux of the image world and imagined exemption from flux in the observer. And what if the image jams. Whack, went my dad's hand on the old black and white TV when the image got stuck in a bodge of crackling lines. I have been having problems with my image processing, I thought I might say up the road at the institution founded by Jonathan Swift. I see the light in the dark and fancy I am moving towards it like a train in a tunnel, but what if the image is the other way round and the tunnel exit is hurtling towards me, beating me back further into the dark. But do the images move in a line or round in a circle, as on the zoetrope; do the images inhabit time or space, independently or overlappingly. I am the boy flipping the corner of the copy-book, but I am the stick man that he flips too, I am all of these things, the self-seeing eye. Walking up towards the hospital I stop in the Augustinian church on Thomas Street and find a blaze of candles lighting up the dark of a side-altar. The church is nearly but not quite empty, and some bustle or other is visible round the main altar. The stained-glass figures here lack the uncanniness of those in the country church: this is the stolid nineteenth century, its Virgin Mary newly manumitted from the Penal Laws and ready to help with your pledge of total abstinence or civil-service entrance exam. Smoke billows from the candles and the image swims before my eyes, exposing the flux beneath the conventional lines. A praying figure on her knees gazes up into the dark, the saints' haloes in the glass tracing an upward line in the glass like bubbles.

§ 11

Out of proportion. My grandmother lies small on the ward at the end of a stone staircase in the rambling old hospital. It is due for demolition. Which will go first though, she jokes. I have come to say goodbye, cheerio for now. The wrapper on a Moo mint takes one, two twists before crinkling onto the coverlet, a shiny nest of the things, and a religious magazine some circulating orderly has dropped on the bed. When she was young she moved across our hometown but her cat decamped and returned to the old house. Come on, she said to the cat on the old railings when she went looking for it, but it perched on the gatepost looking into the distance. I would rather not go. Back to the old house. The school I attended at the end of her road is being demolished. I remember a boy in a bin. When he wanted to punish a child, Brother Justin would put him in an old steel bin and sit on it, ignoring all subsequent bleats and whimpers. Wandering past the classrooms one day I follow a long corridor to a room whence issues a low, rumbling growl, an unknown old brother visible in the room through the open door. He is standing inside a cupboard, face to the wall, repeating a comical mantra, *Next stop Cahirsiveen.* Yet it was from Brother Boniface I learned that Caesar said *alea jacta est* before crossing the Rubicon. Behind the low wall by the bins in the playground a homeless man starts up one morning with a gruff 'Get the hell owwa that!' and shuffles off with his rattling bags. In *Great Expectations* Pip is off to be a gentleman, so why then does he already talk differently from Joe and his sister while still a child. He is a marked man. Something inevitable is taking its course. We do see him still in formation though when he is learning to write. mI deEr JO I opE U r krWItE wEll. Among the categories of letters never sent are those with no addresses and those that have already arrived, since Pip is still at home when he writes it. And how could the boy from the forge not be overcome by Miss Havisham's sprawling ruin. It's not a life, though, no one could live there. Only left-behind people, put there to rot. And yet it casts its spell. Like the great dusty staircases of Mr Jaggers' offices in London, where Pip will again be overcome and feel everything out of proportion. But that too isn't a life. Only out on the marshes is the boy really free. The horizons blotted by prison ships and then the rowboats watching the tide, to slip out to the steamers. What larks. When have I felt most at home. Among the gorse on the Head, the old school visible just beneath me, and overlooking the full wide sweep of the bay where the ferry clears the islands. What larks, I say, straining to see the far hills of the other country through the haze, but it's just a quotation, no one really talks like that.

§ 12

Seeing me in the car waiting to pick him up, my father gives
his habitual salute of a raised finger glancing off his temple.
There you are then. We turn in the poet's drive amid the
workers coming off shift. Bottle of Listerine for you, he says,
as though this were a novelty. They make it by stirring big
vats in their chemical suits. Vats of blood too for the. Swill it
around. Unpleasant whiff off it but the extractor fan picks up
most of that. I'm off then, you mention after the football scores
on the radio, over yonder. Be a nice change of scene for me. My
mother receives the news where she lies semi-prone on the sofa,
straightening up like a mildly surprised corpse on Judgement
Day. Where's that then exactly. Your great-auntie Josie went
there in the 30s, she worked in the polio ward. Still I suppose
you'll be back in a year or two. Goodbye, brothers. Don't think
much of the food on these ferries, I say in The Sportsman Bar
once we have set out together, my parents along for the ride,
I mean, look at that, the soggy end of a veggie burger tipping
out of its bun. Something I've always wondered about the lorry
drivers: they roll on at 10 p.m., down all that drink, then roll
back off at six in the morning. How does that work. Isn't it all
a bit much. Is it enjoyable really or just something they feel
compelled to do. I mean, none of us likes it but here we are.
It's all very agreeable, dad says, once we arrive, of a long line
of tumble-down housing and bargain shops, and cheery soul
that he is means it too. Letting myself into the darkened hall
I pick up some post, which I realise too late is for a namesake
in the flat below. Wouldn't get that at home with a name like
yours. Familiarity amid the strangeness. Then later open the

wrong bin by mistake in the back garden and find a jazz mag. All men too I notice. Bit lurid, the lighting choices. The local poet was known to have kept a collection of mags in his office. Not now preserved, though had they been there would have arisen the question of what to do with them. Slightly jizzed, the catalogue entry could say. Possessed of forensic interest, perhaps. Someone's great-grandmother now, which is to say dead. Semen and dust. Staring from the upstairs window I see my parents climb into the van we hired and drive off into the evening, in time for the overnight ferry crossing and maybe a pint for dad of that lager the lorry drivers liked and a glass for my mother, ah go on. The experience has that holiday feel so they might feel obliged, or maybe it's the having it that makes it feel like a holiday, think of it that way round. A motorway turn-off whizzes past as they drive for the trim suburb where great-auntie Josie ended up, naturalised and suburban, what's she up to these days. And then the great bow-doors opening to receive them like a whale's mouth filtering krill into its dark belly before slipping off into the deep.

§ 13

An ashen-faced woman clutching a pink balloon crosses the road to enter the cemetery. It's somebody's birthday. What I learn from the cemetery is that the death of children today is the saddest thing in the world, but the death of Victorian children was somewhat less so. They died and they died. 'Also . . . child of the above'. I am walking up cemetery road to my workplace, aware behind the fence of the unappealing house where the local poet spent his bloated final years. I am also aware of his partner in life still in situ, camped on a sagging sofa amid a nest of empty bottles, or so I have been informed. Soon afterwards she dies, and soon after that a television programme treats us to a recording of her and the poet drunkenly singing racist ditties together. It was a sorry end. Inhabiting the aftermath of the poet's world and his various regressive attitudes, since they have a knack of lingering on, I am reminded of *Terry and June* and other sitcoms of the 1970s, as pored over by my younger self with near-anthropological awe. Here is the witless sergeant major with the Rover outside and his strong views on the colonies. Here is the dinner party that will go comically wrong when the scatterbrained housewife burns the chops. Here are the rebellious young, all flares and sibeburns, getting it out of their system before taking that steady job at the bank. And how desperately but dependably dull work is. Someone insists on giving you a job for life and putting all that money in your bank account, the rotters. You may dream of running away, but what would you spend the money on anyway and, besides, you'll only slink back in the end, once you get bored. And the porn mag in the desk at work for when you feel a bit, you know. *Terry and June* forever. Maybe the couple from down the street will come round, he wanting to show you the photographs from his golfing holiday and she wanting to talk about how the 'nippers' are getting on. There is no other life. The old man on the crossroads bench wearing a plastic police-man's helmet may not be coming to the party, but he too has his place in the cosmically-ordained feudal pageant. And 'no one actually starves'. Not the man on the bench in town, sit-ting, forever sitting and watching. Oh but I know someone who asked him once if he wanted help, I hear, and he said no. I seek out the poet's house from the other side of the fence, but there is nothing to engage the sweep of my gaze. An ugly garage front stares wall-eyed at the street, and no lace curtain twitches defensively, framing a blank I cannot pass through, turned back on itself and an absence that is nothing and nowhere and endlessly only itself.

§ 14

But no sooner have I established myself here than I am randomly there again. For a brief period there appears to be an open door between the two spaces, as though to go from one to the other were simply a question of travel. So here I am travelling back on whatever pretence that this is a real possibility and not just a piece of self-deception. Yet what I remember is my leaving again, that setting out before dawn once more on my journey east, as though I were a slow learner and hoping to perfect the lesson through force of repetition. The me-of-there has returned, which is to say has not yet left, has reactivated, to make that journey and encounter the me-of-here who awaits him, to feel again that moment of shocked exchange between the old and the new. It is early, there is a touch of frost in the air. My mother is standing in her dressing gown in the porch, there is red wine on my breath from the previous evening, I kiss her on the cheek and watch dimly through the fogged-up window where she lingers as my father reverses out. In the pre-dark dawn the streets are unfamiliar, as though this were a taxi ride to the airport in a town I am visiting for the first time. The news comes on and there is talk of the skulduggery of a well-known public figure. This will not be on the news in the other place, or in the newspaper I will buy in the airport. It fails a certain curiosity test, from the point of view of over there. And with distance comes deformation. A man in a pub tells me a joke about the Irishman with two arseholes. He had a couple of friends; they were inseparable. He is knocked down by a bus. When the ambulance arrives the driver asks for information about the unfortunate Irishman. I don't know much about him on a personal level, says his friend. Wait, there is something, says the other. We went into the chippy there the other evening and the woman said, Here's that Irishman with two arseholes. So in many ways this reflects better on the Irishman than the natives. Is this funny, does that make it better. Debatable. 'Is that part of us': I get that a lot in post offices, that and 'Southern Ireland', where is that. I'm Irish myself though, the man who told me the joke announces, my granny's from Cavan. But with my poor practical skills I now see in the airport I have misread my ticket and mistaken the arrival for the departure time, meaning there is no flight for me to take. My father is probably still outside, paying for his parking before setting out past the airport hotels for the M50. I now have several new destinations to choose from, one of which I will retro-fit to the narrative of the journey I was due to take. Off I go there instead, to struggle with rail times and connections, before arriving late at night, picking up as I enter a large envelope from home with last week's newspaper, posted while I was there but lest, a Post-it note explains, lest I forget.

§ 15

Found, a cat in a cardboard box, behind the Indian restaurant. Small scratch and slither of paws against glass in the RSPCA, then taken home from the smell of disinfectant and the suddenly-looming dogs, who ask only love, who'll have your throat. Through the door of the cat-carrier then, emerging into an unsuspected world. But why stop there. No sooner in the room than vanishes. Where. Not the garden but a hole in the skirting board, where the boiler's small orange flame flickers like a sanctuary lamp. Shifting from ham to ham. Come out pussens, we love you, we hardly know you. But you must go where the doorway leads, in and through. 'It rains', impersonal verb: it 'cats', the house 'cats', conjugates itself afresh. Little machine for habitation. Eyes uncovered behind a book removed from a shelf; there in the window in the evening, then at the door as I open. There are endless cats and there is only one cat. An aspect of cohabitation with a cat is verbal triangulation. I make a remark about or even in the person of the cat, and it is answered in similar spirit; he forms this bridge, unknowing. Meetings with neighbours behind the house after tea for conversations about you, only you, among the bins and the composters, and there you suddenly are slinking by. An available usable language, there for the using, being used. Little black cat my ultrasonic bounced out into the world beyond my ken and reporting back. Yours is the precise depth of an indentation under a bush in the garden, the collar found in a neighbour's bedroom. There are endless houses and there is only one house, but I would like you please to get in this carry-case and come to the vet's. And yours are the dark eyes still that peer from the bars of your portable prison, uncomprehending. In impotent sympathy I would slip through the bars and crouch with you far from the piercing, angry eyes on the bus. Your RSPCA papers name you Salam, after the Indian restaurant, I thought – pint of lager with my curry at the Salam Tandoori, always lager they serve, to make you thirsty – until I remembered Salem, the talking black cat from that show. Then in old age, cat, you have the first of a series of seizures and slowly recover and hunkering down I watch you relearn how to drink, your rough pinky tongue lapping endlessly into your water-bowl. Then that time when there is some disturbance in the garden and you run away, and are not seen again. Until please mister, please mister, says a boy at the door, there is a cat in the woods. We heard him but he wouldn't come out. The best time to attract a lost cat is dawn or dusk, when the light's thin. Go on the prowl for you. But how best attract your attention. I yawp and miaow, just like you, bouncing my need off the trees. And there you are. I lift and scoop. Make for the door with the light in the porch and, quick, you say, as you leap from my arms: in you come, quick, follow me.

§ 16

The trick is knowing how to wedge the books in tight but not too tight. These books have not just followed me round from country to country, but spent all their time together in more or less the same order, among themselves, like an overfed snake coiled round the house. I take down a poetry book by an author filed under M then take care, replacing it later, to slide it in tight against its neighbours. When shelves fill up and books need moving on everything moves, but no sooner is everything in its new place than it has been there always. A new arrival could conceivably come between them, and new books do arrive all the time. Yet when this happens the old relationship continues, the group of two magically subsumed within the newly-formed group of three, and my mental map adjusted accordingly. How consistently are these principles applied. Imperfectly. Now where is that Dickens book. Back at home my mother is keen to empty my study and sends me a slew of photographs of my shelves there. What should she do with all these books. Send them all over, dispatched out into the world and so home. But you/one cannot go home. At the end of *Great Expectations* Pip goes back but he cannot. Much discussion has focused on the end of the book, where he meets Estella by chance in the street and finds her much changed. They talk briefly and part, with Pip putting the past behind him. Dickens' publisher objected to this ending, and in the rewritten version Pip revisits Miss Havisham's house and finds Estella there too, with the implication they will be together at last. But before all this he has gone back to the forge with the intention of proposing to Biddy, only to find her married to Joe. There is a child, called Pip ('We giv him the name of Pip for your sake, dear old chap'). Pip hopes to solve the dramas of the great world by retracting within his concentric circles to the village again and putting things right at source. But the village is not static, and has its own life and momentum. After its spoiling by his unhappy sister, Pip's child-hood home has been put right, but for someone else to inhabit, even if that someone else is 'I again!' But what manner of life will this new Pip have? Will his right beginnings enfold him in the bosom of village life, now it is purged of its cankers? Or will he follow his own narrative of displacement and loss, of journey and return? The world, after all, has not suddenly outgrown its habit of giving us all a good shake. Something I have learned about replacing much-reprinted books, like old Dickens editions, is how tricky it can be to get the same cover. The book is advertised with one cover but you get another. Not good enough. I purchase a replacement copy of one I've mislaid only to receive one with a 'wrong' cover. But then it doesn't fit on my shelf anyway. No, it says, resisting. I am down on my knees pushing away at the bloody thing and it won't go into the gap.

§ 17

But can the portal work backwards as well as forwards, can it open a door not merely into the past but into others' experiences which then become mine? Apparently so. Early on in my stay I have classes in a building that resembles an abandoned tower block, the Loten Building, parts of which I remember as cordoned off, as though no longer fit for human habitation. How surprising then to see a photo of it in the sleeve notes for an album of the guitarist Davey Graham's, who gave a concert at my workplace in 1967, then went and knocked on a student's window at midnight and played another impromptu set in his room, which the student had the presence of mind to record. The album features an ethereal version of 'She Moved Thru the Fair', played in Indian raga style. Only occasionally do the students present pipe up, as when one of them declares 'I must say I'd quite like a song!' I decide that this is the greatest spontaneous artistic event ever to occur in my adoptive city. What a delight to think of artistic performances happening on the strength of a midnight knock, secret epiphanies happening after hours in dark and unfrequented spaces, in the Loten Buildings of this world, caught and preserved accidentally. Graham was the kind of prodigy to whom art comes maybe too easily, in the sense that it must have been a challenge for mere reality to keep up with the soundtrack playing in his head. He lost long years to heroin, and though he got clean did not record again. A man beside me in a pub starts singing sea shanties – 'I shipped on board of a Liverpool liner . . .' – beating time on his knee with a set of spoons. A poet at a restaurant meal, ill at ease in company, produces a tin whistle and walks up and down as he plays it. A friend with a guitar knocks on the door late in the evening and sits on the floor singing, continues doing so when left alone as I walk to the shop for wine. I once shared a stage with Ali Farka Touré, he announces. I've got a class in the morning, I say. His percussionist sat on the floor beating a wooden block. The thing about the musicians here is they don't know how good they are, the guitarist says, the best ones. They won't put themselves forward but then they might sing a song when everyone else has stopped and it will be the best thing you've heard all night. I could tell you their names . . . I can't remember their names. Yes, he says, I know 'She Moves Through the Fair'. It goes like this. You've got to listen out for the midnight knock on the window. And let them in. But this performance goes unrecorded. I have a class in the morning. But what's that constantly shifting time signature. What's the time. What is time.

§ 18

Biroed onto the soft wood of the bird-hide on the riverbank is a spunking knob. I count four upwardly-propelled drops of spunk before the artist acknowledged the force of gravity and allowed the stream to descend, with another four trailing away to one side. A strong sensation of living on the seabed, of the ground falling away beneath my feet. The fields on the estuary aspire to, yearn for sea-level. A container ship scuds past with only the containers and the bridge visible, then twice a day the ferry's floating bauble, close enough to swim out to, past the redshanks' and curlews' riddling tracks in the mud. What do they make in the plant, all flares and smells, framed behind the field of rapeseed by the boatyard and the church at the end of the street? Demeter repurposed as the goddess of agriculture and heavy industry, breeding bioethanol fuel from fermented sugar and sorcery. A wind turbine cranks in a garden at the end of the field, amid generations of discarded tractors and fridges. The field is upsizing, capsizing into the sea. Continue east in search of the breach point, where the water comes over the road. Here on the spit, the long accusing finger, the land falls away on the east but banks up on the west. Travel to Aldbrough where sea monsters have taken huge chunks from the cliffs, snacking on dogs and their walkers as they do so, and the sea coughs up discarded ordinance. Do not approach. Good place to move with a terminal disease, something fast and painful, with a view of the oil fields named for lost villages, of which this will soon be one. I think of what roots people in a place, but what roots a place in a place: put an ear to the ground and hear it moving, if you listen hard enough. Yet the edge, the edge of precariousness, has its advantages too. The village at the end of the spit is a nest of pirates. Boats cannot turn into the estuary without the villagers skimming off their share. And then comes the breach and the sea too claims its share. Much later, boats still cannot enter the estuary on their way back from whaling trips without running into press-gangers, keen to send the whalers off to the Napoleonic wars. So the sailors get out at the point and walk home instead. Mutable land means safety and camouflage. Perhaps in the future the whole region will be reduced to a patchwork of islands and isthmuses, narrow strips above the sunken fields and grave-yards. Unless I am slow in noticing and this has already taken place. Home. Shop. Workplace. What have I seen or touched here that lies beyond that. I am peering over the edge when I look through the fog and all my wanderings, whispers the worm in my skull, have been on fixed paths leading nowhere. Then turning to retrace my steps on the crumbling coast I see the path has fallen away, and another figment has dissolved, and I am pushed onwards through the curtain of fog and the spray from the everywhere-encroaching sea.

§ 19

Not this place again. But yes. Short stroke, short stroke from the Kish, wait for the long one and: there, now. I have returned to the original east and am looking out to sea at the lighthouse pointing the way to that further east where you had come with me only for us to wash back here on the tide. Busy old clock on the wall, that I remember, beating out time like a robot conductor, parcelling the afternoon into small, twitching chunks. The self-deceiving belief that at difficult moments time will stop, and frame your moments for your closer study and understanding. In reality there is stasis and progress at once, a long note in the fugue stretto while the noises off of everyday life keep playing against it. But does Bach ever write a fugue that comes unstuck and unzips itself before our ears. Or is it just that inexorable purposefulness of his. Do you ever take a day off from this, this mental performance. It seems not. Our duet has failed. The small low harbour is served by a retinue of hyperactive forklift trucks, describing elegant arcs along the short pier, sometimes preserved in a scout's knot of tyre-marks. Later, a seal will arrive and hoist itself out of the water to perform theatrical begging routines in front of the fish-shop. Hand gestures I remember, there are hand gestures during our exchanges tracing patterns of eloquent impetration and rage. When St Patrick put ashore here first, the locals came to stone him, knocking out one of his follower's teeth. Following the toothy line of the coast on a wordless walk I feel the stones rain down. Visible again through the clouds the Kish resembles the siren on top of the world's slowest police car, our emergency both urgent and nobody's business. But one enfolds and contains another. The bus station in the city implies this town, when I see it again, the one place leads to the other. And on the bus from the city, which I do not suppose I will be taking again, the driver would often stop at a long farmhouse by the road and vanish inside for a few moments, leaving the engine running. But here I am in my original east who will shortly journey again over there to resume my station. The forklift trucks, as noted, get very close to the water while never misjudging the edge. How does one stop oneself tipping over. Something happens to stop it. Impersonal. I do something to stop it. Something is done. By me or to me. Baffling. Convenient. Hopeless. Is it all just one big game to you. I stand a little longer looking at the gunmetal grey of the sea. My sea, your sea, the dog's sea, down by the marshland past the railway tracks. What's that on the stones. Is it lovers. The fucking cheek. And further off a woman trailing her feet in the water like a child. But the dog. I would like to say goodbye to the dog.

§ 20

Where is red. The walls were red. It has painted me over. My dwindling is growing. I take a brush and move the past around on the wall. A hole for towels. I call that the press. Say for be said, cypher be said. I sat on my hands. It is an interior. It was manoeuvred into place. When you are finished they will come and take it away. A hawk in the garden digs a pigeon a grave. Wears her wings like a cape. The house is one big brick. Rain falls like blood. Where are my compass points, have they come along too. I am, we're at the top of something, we all dip our feet in the river. I slipped on the ice and left my elbow behind. Only the break came away with me. These footpaths will have me, they know what they're doing. The sunsets were standard, they'll see you right. What is that hook for on a cat's paw. Life's little coat-hangers. On me too hang your hat. A fuck on the stairs, I fucked the stairs. Closer and closer apart. I wrote with my teeth. What cannot be said, what cannot. Pointing and not understanding pointing. It's a finger. How to get past that. Signs cannot point at themselves and yet there they are. There is a body, fresh and waiting, can it be mine. Eventlessness is sometimes a theme, the diary of a disappointment. The neighbour ran past but not running, it's not running unless you change your clothes. These are the rules and with a face drawn on. Rearrange all the background. Eclectic velleities of the endurable. Nice to doll it up a bit, 'velleities'. Simply engulfed in tofu. Cat thinks he wants it but doesn't. The spine is an instrument, what tune is it playing for me now. Bleaches and poisons always to hand when I'm doing the dishes. When I have finished with the smile I gave it away. A lifelong struggle with bins and their bags. You never see a nun on the streets. Nice to come and spend the weekend though. But who. Who come. Strange but when the train passed under the bridge I found myself lowering my head. I entered the village and found scarecrows everywhere. Daylight sleeps in a box. If there are no mountains then build some. When the trawler sank one man got free and floated on a raft to Iceland. He found a farmhouse and stood all night by the window not wanting to lie down and die. When he came home he knew he would go to sea again but did not talk about what happened. What cannot. Safer be said. A flux of falling away and coming together again. Fingers pressed to my temples, still today to see that line of horizon waiting to tip me back from my own high seas to behind that thin lace curtain. A dream of the North Sea carried on tides of sobs in the storm drains and underground rivers.

§ 21

Another phrase used by the local poet that gave me much pause
over the years: 'cut-price crowd'. It is a cut-price crowd. We are
a cut-price crowd. They are a cut-price crowd. People are poor,
their houses are small, they might have no garden. Granted. A
shirtless young man shouting an invitation across the street to
a young woman to come back to his place proclaims 'Ah ehn't
got no diseases or owt.' You want to make something of it? But
I am being biographical, mistaking the voice of the poem for
the voice of the poet. I am mistaking the voice of the poet for
the attitude I am reading into the phrase. These attitudes were
common at the time. I am mistaking the attitude I read into
this phrase for what the poem wants me to take away. And
what's that then. It is a cut-price crowd. There is a tone of studied neutrality. It is the default, it has no identity. It is a social-
realist gesture. It could be anyone talking, it could be the young
man you saw. Tom Courtenay was from the Hessle Road. The
syntax in context is ambivalent. Poems are not spoken by
actual people. They do not have paraphrasable things to say,
or attitudes as such. These things are merely there, so much
raw material, drawn from the merely-thereness of the social
envelope. A sneering poem could be read as a subtle critique of
that sneer. Who are we to say that some racist doggerel is not
a withering satire on racism. No? It is a performative gesture.
Who is this poem talking about then. It is a cut-price crowd. Is
that us. Is it them – 'them'. Have they been told. What might
they think. But which of these worlds do I inhabit. The builder
comes and pulls up my floorboards. What's this then, he won-
ders aloud. There has been some subsidence. Many of these

houses were built without proper foundations. They are sinking into the ground. I retreat to a back bedroom while he takes over the house. In the morning when I come down his helper, the builder's mate, is often there before him. I find him standing drinking tea in the unrecognisable kitchen, sheets everywhere and what is that smell, is it turps, is it sealant or gypsum. Sometimes the builder's face appears at the window, where he needs to poke around in the guttering. Quick, acknowledge and draw the curtains. I understand little of the process, but am happy to stand in the kitchen while he explains it, and maybe chew a biscuit too, out of politeness or whatever. One day he opens up some panel or other under the sink and asks me to come have a look. I stare down into the subterranean space, sniffing some manner of noisome mulch. That's your problem, he says, you don't want to be seeing that, flicking his torch around he looks and studies it closely, masses of it right there, unbearably so. Let's just get rid of it now, I say, jocose-assertively, I'll pay you good money to get that stuff out of my face.

§ 22

Tarkovsky's *Solaris* is a very long film, full of meditative pauses and silences, but one such scene that has always stood out for me is Burton's futuristic drive home from Kelvin's house towards the start of the film. Kelvin is about to travel to investigate the unusual events at the space station orbiting the planet Solaris, and Burton wants to warn him what to expect. His reports of monstrous visions – a giant baby – have brought him humiliation and ridicule from the authorities. Though Kelvin's experiences will soon completely change him, for the moment he is bullish. There is an argument, after which Burton storms out. Burton's car is driverless, and he maintains a distracted, faraway expression on the route home. Cars slip alongside his, peel off in different directions, negotiate flyovers and pass through tunnels. Even as I refresh my feelings on the dystopian-futuristic Soviet landscape this represents, I notice from some passing signs that the scene has been shot in Japan. At one point a car resembling a taxi appears in the right of shot. Keep an eye on it. We abruptly cut from the car to Kelvin's garden, where he is burning photographs while talking to his parents of other, more important photographs, filed away in his room. We also catch a glimpse of a framed photo in the house of Hari, his late wife, a hallucination of whom will haunt his time on the space station, before her final exorcism. These scenes are poised and exquisite, but full of stored-up turmoil, even when Kelvin is merely standing watching the swaying eelgrass under the surface of the pond. When the scene ends it does so again abruptly, and we have made the shift into space. But what of Burton, I ask myself. In the recording he plays of his

43

presentation to his superiors, he is a much younger man. He is now bald and walks with a cane. Has he been in disgrace ever since? One of his superiors suggests he is 'unwell', in the familiar Soviet euphemism, suggesting imminent non-personing and disappearance. But one of the young children playing in the garden is his, and during the car journey the child appears playfully behind his father's back. On the space station, Hari both is and isn't real. When mocked for being a hallucination she kills herself, only to regenerate. The unreality of her death raises questions about how real she has ever been, or has been allowed to be, whether in hallucination form or before that. There is an element in the film of indulged male agony and female unreality, the terrible psychodrama of emotional martyrdom, inarticulacy, sacrifice and immolation. The film ends with a resolution that is not a resolution, suggesting Kelvin remains a deeper prisoner of his hallucinations than he can understand. But his is only one journey. Burton has travelled to the space station and swapped it for other journeys, other destinations. His car is driverless and knows where he needs to be. It takes its place unexceptionally on the road alongside others. We do not need to be told where he is going, perhaps because he has escaped all this fiasco, and his happiness writes white, as Montherlant said. Is he happy? He is well off out of it. A car resembling a taxi appears in the right of shot, colour leaks into this long black-and-white sequence, and the briefly-glimpsed car turns red.

§ 23

I have come to suspect the city is some manner of space station afloat on a sea of my dreaming. What lies beyond it, I wonder, what waking reality is my trance denying me. The street map, the map in the car, the railway map, are Vitruvian man in his hoop, an external circulatory system round which I am propelled in search of myself. There was a line to the coast, but no more, though the Station Road remains the Station Road, a steam train tearing down the torn-up line on the pub sign. I have established that the emptiest map square in the country is just over here: I see an electricity pylon and a pheasant. My turning up like this threatens to distort all meter readings, however, so I have endeavoured to be as little here as possible. I turn from the estuary and the majestic muddy flow of the Humber to a tributary, the Ancholme. And here is a toll-bridge over its modest flow, with a man cupping his hand to receive a twenty-pence piece to allow me to cross. I write this in the present tense, but a double present, interrupting this narration now to look up what bridge this might be and failing to find it. Am I hallucinating it? Do you get a lot of passing traffic, I ask, but he waves me away, now is not the moment for chit-chat. I flow over the territory, down larger to ever smaller back-roads and rivulets, aiming only to get off the grid entirely, subdividing into myself and the one true place. But can the map show or contain what lies beyond it, I wonder. In Hitchcock's *The 39 Steps*, there is a scene in which Hannay escapes his pursuers through a buffet car on a train, requiring elaborate evasive manoeuvres from a waiter bearing a tray over his head. No sooner has he completed the manoeuvre to avoid Hannay than he must repeat it to avoid the police too. In a more recent film, we would have a close-up of the waiter's face, and the tension would dissolve into a passing moment of light relief. Hitchcock chooses not to do this, and the feats of nimble-footedness are made to seem routine, as though performed by an insect. In coming here I thought I was performing some elaborate fandango off the beaten track, but I see now this was just my track all along. A collar on the blue cat playing at my feet in the shadow of the huge cement works announces her name as Babushka. Occasionally drivers following the beaten track of their satnav will drive up and become stuck in dead-ends, or off the ends of bridges, what the satnav says being in some sense more real, to them at least, than what their eyes are telling them. I turn back from the trickle of the Ancholme to the Humber and continue my journey upriver to its unknowable source (the Humber has no source).

§ 24

Then sometimes at night the impulse to purchase a bottle of wine, sudden whim to have it pass through me on its way somewhere else, on its journey, sometime between the hour of laying down books and giving up for the day, the better to help me give up. My end of the street is a dead end, with a little laneway or ginnel named after St Ninian, apostle to the Picts and the north, cutting through to the road beyond and the shop on the other side. And then to one side as I walk a railway line, leading off to the east of the city and the docks. On a dark night to be walking along with the ground shaking at the approach of the train and in a nearby window the green light of a fish tank. Do they offer much comfort, I wonder, is someone there watching them now, where is the love though, with a fish. And not just St Ninian, walking into history along his ginnel, but a Jewish cemetery too, just beyond, behind a high fence, inscriptions in Hebrew visible through the bars, and will I buy red or white, and a packet of crisps as well, why not. An owl clears his throat in a sycamore tree overhead, setting off a chain reaction of owls all down the street. And then to approach my door again on the trek back, crisps eaten, and confront the joy of my setting out, the expectation still intact of my joyful return, and what's this, a bottle of wine in a plastic bag and a sore head in prospect, and only the black cat's face at the window watching as I approach to haul this back from farce into love, sudden deep pangs of love for the helplessness of it all. My window frames are rotten, reach into them and you could pull out whole handfuls, while into my porch blow passing leaves and collect, for a spell, a brief spell, before blowing on, on their way.

The postman sometimes leaves letters in the porch, sometimes takes the extra step and pushes them through the letterbox, but never through the low-set porch letterbox, this is a step too far, or should I say too few. What else happens in my porch-portal: my moments, the porch's moments. There is a concavity, that sense again of slow sinking into the ground. One day I see some boys go past on their rag-and-bone cart, drawn by a poor old nag, steam rising from her haunches, and out I dash to photograph them, picaresque spectacle that they make. Would you give us some money mister, one asks, drawing himself up and preening amid his cargo of bedposts and bicycles. I'll give you a pound. A pound each, he insists, so I do. I strain to catch the horse's glance behind her blinkers, but then she tosses her head and is off, watched by me from the porch as she retreats down the street, and I carry the moment with me through the gap of my open front door, that and the sheaf of letters a passing postman presses into my hand.

§ 25

I am walking home in the dark one evening when you cross my path ahead of me, crossing the road, then are lost to view again on the other side. Is it the convention to run after and accost. Best leave it for now. But not long. Come back the next day. There you are then. The man in the shop by your house lines up a row of fridges along your garden wall every day and sits on one, saluting the passers-by. The freckles on your face match a scatter of clouds over the estuary seen from a train window early one morning. I left at the milkman hour to come here, you will say later, and sped past John Clare's initials where he carved them into a bridge. Is that black cat yours, I would ask, he just sits in the road. There was something I wanted to ask. In the novel we like. Yes. Go on. The one with the man alighting early from the tram to the station. There is no stop but he gets off, then continues in the same direction. The same thing keeps happening to me with the bus for round the corner. I press the button and realise too late the driver will be stopping a stop ahead of where I want. But I'd rather not explain myself, so I get off anyway and keep going. Yes, I've done that too, you say. But you live right here, it's two minutes away. Not all journeys start from here. I wouldn't start from here, as the joke says. From where then. But you can't go back. And where are you from. Originally. All over. Rather not say. You go on to go back. You go on and find where you start from has changed. Should we give it a try. Try a long walk. Have you been down this way, by the river. What would bring me there, you say. Nothing. Exactly. Of course I have. That book we like though, with the man and the tram, what does it mean. To you. The language of the academy now, to speak of that, it comes with a certain violence, like a steel glove patting a butterfly. I resist it and wonder whether the right way to read isn't just to drift round the place sitting on cemetery walls or railway embankments absorbing a sentence here, a sentence there, underlining a phrase over an afternoon drink to the background click-clack of men playing dominoes. Yes, that it is the way. No Jehovahs, they shout at us once, seeing us enter the pub with a pile of books. The first edition is full of mistakes. I suspect the printers couldn't read English. If it is in English even, really. And yet I find the mistakes strangely lovable. I see them and think, I know what you mean. We hear what we say/each of us says and think, I know what you mean. Who else can say as much. Billions. And yet. I could show you the book. Is that a thing then, you say, or I say, with comic naïveté, is that a thing. A little private study session. What are we doing though. We see a line take off into the distance and decide to follow it. But I wouldn't start from here. Well off we go then.

§ 26

A pigeon in an inside coat pocket lined with bird-seed. At full time the score was tied to the pigeon's leg and the bird released, to be first to bring the news home. Or so I am told. When were you last in a crowd of ten thousand, be they pigeons or people. There is naturally a limit to your freedom to act. At a certain point the street becomes a queue for your seat. You may purchase refreshments and stand at a trough among fellow urinators but otherwise the sitting and leaning and stamping and standing will be localised on your plastic seat. Someone sings a song because the man next to him does so too, and he in turn has done so only because of the man next to him. Yet without you the crowd is nothing, here where the absolute meets the singular. Football is a simple game. From this distance it can be hard to make out the players' faces. A player in red makes a run from midfield and is instantly recognisable from his posture of splayed, raised elbows and head slightly lowered and thrust forward. If you took away the ball and the teams still covered the pitch like that, the systole-diastole of their formations and the invisible patterns they inscribe on the turf would be art. French symbolist poetry, splicing the pre-ordained onto the random. Advance declined, tilted by one or the other edge. Even when thrown into eternal circumstances from the bottom of a shipwreck. The manoeuvre grasping the edge of the unanimous horizon. Goal. Keep your seat. And out we stream, thinning out slowly at every junction, reabsorbed into the myriad back-streets. I think of L. S. Lowry and his street scenes, from the other side of the Pennines though they be. An aspect of Lowry's work is that his figures can seem to be undifferentiated, faceless stick-people enacting their assigned roles. His avoidance of close-up portraits can give the impression of Lowry's lacking an active role in the scene he depicts and preferring to keep his distance. Even in a painting like *The Funeral Party*, none of the figures acknowledges anyone round them, but stand about in mute disconnection. Lowry's politics were it seems traditional working-class Tory. In later life Lowry received a letter from a teenaged girl asking advice on becoming an artist. He befriended her family and, having no family of his own, eventually left her everything in his will. On his death she was taken to a bank vault and shown a series of drawings. Her first thought was 'Oh no, no not Uncle Laurie', followed by 'They are me.' With their constricting and punitive images of a naked young woman, the drawings have an undoubted sadistic quality. The stick-people in his street scenes often have no faces because they do not rise to the level of individuated personhood. The stick-people in his street scenes often have no faces because in our banally unremarkable suffering we are better off without them.

§ 27

Any man beyond the age of twenty-six who finds himself on a bus can count himself a failure, said Margaret Thatcher. That twenty-six is oddly specific, I always thought. Nevertheless, bus journeys are not always pleasant experiences. That house over there, one bloke upstairs on a bus tells another: that's where I go when I need a gun. I don't know that I believe him, and suspect his performance has something to do with the captive audience his fellow passengers provide. A student who worked in a bookie's tells me of a man coming in to rob him with what he claimed was a gun under a tea towel. Some grabbing later by a have-a-go hero reveals the weapon to be a banana. I am told of a bank robber who made good his escape by bicycle, perhaps having blown his budget on the hold-up weapon. Gun crime is rare. But the guns are out there, in a bottom drawer somewhere, or under a brick in a back garden. Have you ever held a gun in your hand, would you know what to do. Guns, guns, guns. Colin here beside me in the pub was in 'the province' and met Bobby Sands. He was a right character. Colin's mate was standing beside him when he took a shot to the head. Were you scared, I ask. Not as much as I was of my ex-wife, Pat. Oh, was her name Pat then. You either take the banter or don't. There is that performative aspect to it. No offence mate. Are we on a level here. Joe the soldier, who likes reciting Owen and Sassoon in his cups, has gone away, then turns up with a gun on the front of the *Mirror*, face blacked out. He is in Libya with some mercenaries and is recognised from his tattoos. What sort of people were they, I ask him later. A great bunch of lads. I was in a war you know, as Edward says in *The*

League of Gentlemen. You come back knocked about a bit but with your funny stories and catch-phrases. The taxi driver has been in a war. In some ways here it's worse. The first place they sent me, the man in my room was a spy. Spies came with us to send back reports. Here I opened the door and the man threw a brick. Where are your women, they ask. Someone said, where is your wife and I [*the 'search me' hand gesture*]. You are making the crossing and someone tells you to go over there, so you do and then . . . My country is forbidden. Why do you have a phone, the man asked me, angry, he thought I should have nothing. Help me, is all I want. His friends needed help, so Bob thought why not. I know a bloke who knows a bloke, says the man on the bus. These things can be arranged. You didn't hear it from me, that's all. And this bloke you . . .? Consider it done.

§ 28

With his frequently raised eyebrow and physical disconnection, Kelvin makes for a poor action-hero cosmonaut in *Solaris*. And truth be told, he does little enough. On his arrival in the station no one comes to meet him; his surprise at this is perfunctory, as is his response to the run-down state in which he finds the ship. He knocks on Dr Snaut's door and there is a brief exchange in which Snaut mentions that one of the other two cosmonauts has died. He then fobs Kelvin off, telling him to return the next day, and warns him to be on the look-out for hallucinations. All who allow themselves to get close to Solaris will be prey to a return of the repressed, which quickly becomes all-consuming, cancelling all thoughts of the practical side of Kelvin's mission. On some readings of the film, Tarkovsky is performing a critique not just of Kelvin's necrophiliac masculinity but the nature of our interpersonal relations. We are radically alone; we reify and instrumentalise the other, reducing them to figments of our morbid needs and desires. While this might be true of Kelvin's relationship with Hari, I wondered about the rest of his life. Kelvin and his line manager back at home, Kelvin and his town councillors. Ah, but I'm being arch. His minor personal relationships are already reified and there was never any question of them being anything more. In that case, why not have them stalk the corridors of the space station too: a Kafkaesque allegory laying bare his agonies through banal daily interactions rather than the emotional abattoir of his reunion with Hari. One also notes his non-response when the manifestations of Snaut and Sartorius's hallucinations (that dwarf) are visible or escape from their rooms. It's understood: there will be manifestations all round; they will be morbid and best ignored; they are no one else's business but the dreamer's; we are all alone. If this is just how normal life is anyway, why all the razor-edge drama on a space station — why not paint these lessons by the kitchen sink back on earth? It's not the same then, implicitly. How did you know where I was? he asks Hari early on after their encounter. I have to see you all the time, she says, refusing to be parted from him. But where is a ghost's right place, really. If the ghost spends all her life there, and now I am here, does she come too. Or does she remain behind waiting. For the return. Since the film ends with a return. Back to the old house. Far from the estranging, radioactive sea. But, it turns out, in the middle of that sea (the house is). He hasn't gone back at all. To return is to go on. To go on is to return. Is this a paradox. No. Where am I leading you. Where are you leading me. Perhaps we are there already.

§ 29

Sits on his hands, Mike. In his seat by the fire. Stokes the fire.
Knows how to rake and keep it lit. People bring wood. Bits of
furniture, old pallet wood from the yards. We roast chestnuts
on it one Christmas, a Dickensian moment. A lot of baldy bas-
tards in tonight, says bald John. What have you got in your bag
you bastard, he asks someone else, always the matey 'bastard'.
Meat, some meat. Mike drinks a mix of Landlord bitter and
Neckoil. Father had been a pub pianist: I found his grave in
the city's eastern cemetery, in among the plague victims and
in earshot of the prison exercise yard. Mike makes me think of
Bohumil Hrabal and the narrative, myth perhaps, of the holy
drinker, the social drinker rather than the outright alcoholic,
though as for the latter who knows. I like to enter by the M&R
sign at the side, even if I have approached by the front door,
ducking past the dartboard on my way in. Good arrows! Once
on a lamppost outside I see a perching cormorant. If you turn
up at lunchtime you can get free drinks, I work out, when a new
barrel is getting put in and the run-off has a bit of a head on it. I
say 'you' could, though obviously not just anyone. Lined up on
the counter by the glued-down snuff box for consumption *gratis*.
Cricket on in the afternoon and then the rugby and football
after that, Alex sat in his armchair, the northern 'sat', if you
please. A fault-line runs through the city's memory, between
what remains of inner-city life and the satellite estates people
were moved to in the 60s and 70s. Old trawlermen playing
dominoes, old memories of the cod wars. I could tell when the
skipper came in that time Rick and the others thought he were
a right bastard, that word again. Mike, to me you represent the

world of social realism, a world I realise is not merely there as a given, but to be built and entered, prepared for in the mind. 'There presses in . . . what concentrates down in the warm hollow.' It presses in, as the low ceiling presses down, intimately. The tides in the river can do strange things to the cellar, from which reminders of its moods will occasionally waft. The space is its own archive, with its roll of honour of former curates. Mike has died. I don't want you going round to Mike, says the barmaid when I come in, he's not there. Afterwards he gets a plaque and a photo, for having sat there and drunk. Is this an achievement. Yes. Social realism. Builds a world. Frail, not immutable. Departs. Chase it, it's not coming back. I watch Alan descend to the cellar for a barrel. *Facilis descensus averno*, bit of Latin for you. Come back up Alan, we need you. D'you want another. No stay there, I'll go, I'll go.

§ 30

Contemplating absences that are nothing and nowhere and endlessly only themselves, I often think of another line of the local poet's, about life coming and going without our understanding why, and all because of 'what something hidden from us chose.' Why did I come here, I ask myself. I don't really know. Should I leave. No. Should I move fifty miles down the line. You can't. The bay window in the kitchen leaks. It rains and the damp comes right in, but I can't get a man in, am too paralysed to pick up the phone. It will get fixed, eventually, I tell myself, never mind how. I notice an aversion to taking the initiative or acknowledging agency, says the worm in my brain, what's that about. But things do happen, you've just given a rather large example. The window? No, coming here in the first place. But you seem to dissociate yourself from change, why is that. No, I'm not defending it. To return to the poet though, I continue. Don't change the subject, I'm not changing it, hear me out. There is a stylised passivity, most often in the face of death ('Death is no different screamed at than withstood'), but which spreads back over the rest of life too, and which we are meant to find, if not exactly admirable, then . . . inevitable. Why is that. Well, I know a man, I said. Someone has published a book, a woman has translated Homer, and in my presence he says 'Nothing for the white male here then', and I wonder what that means. I mean, the woman is white too. It means something has changed but he can't, the study of literature is white males, and why are they changing it ('they') – what do they want from him, what do they expect him to do. He didn't ask to be a white male, he says, though he is the one

59

who has brought the subject up; it must be another thing that 'something hidden' from him chose. So why are they ('they') making a fuss. But how, how are they. By a woman writing a book, why not write a book while male instead, why are they being so hostile. So much of life, I learn, is about squatting, toad-like, on what you have and refusing to give ground, then asking 'why are you doing this to me', as though it's their fault. And on top of that to present it as something beyond your control, as though your pettiness had the same force of inevitability as a diagnosis of inoperable cancer of the oesophagus. Can I interrupt here, interjects the worm in my brain. Did you ever get the bay window fixed. Yes. No. I did but it started again. What will you do. I don't know. What is your point here. The squatting toad, who won't engage and can't be bothered, is me. I see. Not about the woman writer – I mean, come *on* – I mean in general, the petulant obstinacy and not being able to get past it. So about that leak. Well. I put buckets and towels down. In the bay window. When water comes in I put a bucket on the floor and a line of tea-towels round the glass. It seems to help.

§ 31

The bird-hide is an eye, I am grit in the aqueous humour, I
draw the back of my hand over my eyelid and see clearly at
last. The gaze strains forward but also retreats to the binocu-
lars' eyes-behind-eyes. With their double foveas, birds of prey
can see insects on the ground from the top of tall trees. Strand
upon individual strand I watch the whimsical eelgrass sway
round the edges of the pond where redshanks and avocets
pick their way through the shallows. Among the phenomena
I have become familiar with, from long hours sitting in the
hide, is what we might term the 'renunciatory downgrade'. It's
a marsh harrier, I announce, but no, it's a buzzard. As though
a buzzard were not also a joyous thing to behold. One way of
countering this would be to announce 'look, a pigeon' repeatedly as I walk down the street, a small liberationist gesture.
Look, it's nothing at all. Time passes, and still waiting for a bittern, as I have been doing for some years now, I watch a heron
descend, resembling nothing so much as a man attempting to
find his footing on the rungs of a ladder. Bitterns were once a
game bird, predation driving them to extinction in Britain in
later Victorian times, and though now indubitably here – their
springtime boom audible for miles around – they wisely prefer
to remain unseen, even the bitterns just a few yards from me
now. Their (invisible) hunch puts me in mind of a put-upon
scribe, a Bartleby of the reedbanks, who would 'prefer not to'.
Is it cryptogeography, my love of the creatures that are there
and aren't, loved for their evading of my gaze and what could
only be the disappointment of seeing them at last. In Australia
the ground-nesting night parrot had been presumed extinct for

a century when a dead bird was found in 2006. Then nothing, then nine years later a live bird is seen. It is an, on the face of it, unremarkable budgerigar-like thing. On Tasmania, zealots comb the bush for the thylacine, a carnivorous marsupial last seen in a zoo in 1936. I assume this search is driven on some level by guilt, though if so why, I wonder, does the thylacine-chaser I read about speak of his desire to find one and cage it. To what end. Sir Thomas Browne kept a bittern in his study, the better to study its boom. The yellow-green splayed feet are superb, inelegant though larger birds can often appear when they walk. Somewhere amid its tracts of abstraction and Hegel parody, Kierkegaard's *The Concept of Anxiety* mentions the vast nothingness of the Jutland bogs, from which now and then a pheasant will rear up. (A bittern, an actual bittern rears up, flies past the hide in an instant.) The philosopher's thoughts rear up in similar style, he suggests, to the startled game bird, amid so much vacancy. But how far will they get. The concept of being perceived as a totality-category splashes back down to earth where a vole disappears into the riverbank with the bittern somewhere behind it. A dream of perpetual concealment returns sulkily to lurking in the reeds. But if the bittern is seen even once he is seen for all time.

§ 32

The thing about going under the water is the not knowing where you will surface. Whose legs are those, whose face do I make out peering at me, down unseeing through the water. In the lobby I am given small blue plastic bags of overshoes, in which I clump to the poolside and its changing rooms; the locker key is on the end of a bent pin, which I hook through my togs. Around the city are dotted half a dozen pools, from the leisure centre and its hellpit of youths, to the featureless overlit cube, to the Victorian philanthropist's dream of a chlorinated commonweal. Paddling laboriously up and down I let my thoughts slip into a gently amniotic rhythm. Dribbles of water run off down the plug-holes, but how much at once, are we at risk of it all flushing away and leaving us thrashing on the pool floor. Swimming by my side you execute deftly athletic tumble-turns and front-crawls, a waterborne lifeform far beyond my stage of adaptation. But what I love about water is the sense of moving, thinking, in a medium, and sculpting myself from my environment as I go. I scissor-kick and think that scissor-kick's thought, it is some lines of Stevie Smith's about floating on a river where it hinges upon the perfected sleep of perfect images. I plough the water forty times and the images sown in my head will sprout with me when I clamber out. I add up the distances and make a kilometre, and dream of kilometre-long swimming pools, of long canals replacing the car-congested streets outside. Come heavy rains, floods and turloughs are born in dips in the road, under railways bridges, in odds and ends of fields beyond the city limits. A pipe bursts in the attic and the ceiling plaster collects to a blister before bursting over the bookshelves beneath. A flood defence bursts and the map is redrawn. Tall boats once anchored in the city-centre park and will again. The pool water cries out to the encroaching water all around, they long to be joined. All my hours in the pool spill over, join up with the time I climbed to Lough Bray in the hills of my youth, stripped off and swam across it, sensing the conical depths of its dark waters far beneath my feet. While swimming, I reach out and touch, not knowing what it will be. Approaching the end of my length, I have to touch the edge, even if it means swimming round a stationary swimmer, I must feel those tiles under my fingers. But it is Friday evening and I am the last swimmer left. The life-guard slumps bored in her high-chair. How long will he keep going, she must wonder, is there an end in sight. I am there and not yet there. I go under one last time not knowing where I will surface. At night the swimming pool will look perfectly static but carry my imprint under its surface, my small, absorbed commotion the secret lie it carries at the heart of its stillness.

§ 33

During the great infection it will be someone's role to die nameless and go in the mass-grave behind the cemetery, who will that be. Dirty tenement water cupped in their hands, their chapels overrun in the Gordon riots. Then reborn in the Victorian Gothic of the church of St Charles Borromeo, its splendid interior and the parish priest rising above the altar and the cholera pits at the Last Judgement. In my friend's poem he shares a fire with a woman from the old country, her English improving to the point of nodding along to tales of the bargeist stalking the yard for surplus children to carry off. The people I meet from the old country tend to be working-class, in the sense that if not, then enough time has passed to knock the old country out of them and send them vanishing upwards into assimilation. Or they remain citizens of the old country, but a version of it standing in shadows behind the actual place. An old country priest signs my passport application under a portrait of the pope, arms spread and cape billowing wide. His house is full of bottles of whiskey. I ask him why and he responds, because he does not drink. I who never met Travellers in the homeland talk to Travellers in the pub by the tyre-yard. Have you heard tell of the Dorans, you'd see them everywhere you went at fairs and funerals. And then to hear of the singer who comes from the west to the east – the old country's east – then from there went east again, over the sea, to a 'white rose town in love with roads'. He works on the roads and sends word after a year for his family to come join him. He plays the button accordion in the house. For a year after that he is still dressing out of a suitcase from the floor instead of a wardrobe. There is a house on the M62, the motorway goes round it. Seeing it he would think of himself, in but not of the stream of things here. One story has it the farmer wouldn't sell. Not so. There was a fault on the land, so the navvies dug round it. They sweated blood and they washed down mud. How would you describe *sean-nós* singing, asks the interviewer. They were mad for the music in this place, but the *sean-nós* doesn't come across so well in the club, so he didn't like performing, says his daughter. The first we knew of his singing was when we heard it on the radio. There was always something missing for him though. Do you still think that. No. Yes. I'd like to go back and see if it's still there. Over there. Home. When you've music in you, you're hearing music always. What do you think about when you think about home. All the roads. Just the roads, to walk along them and see where they'd lead.

§ 34

Go along with you then, is it, you say, and off we go north. This, then, is the intensest rendezvous. When we sit on the train, staring out the window in different directions, are we still of one mind on this journey of ours. But what if life is not a journey, and it is we who stay still while the landscape is wheeled past. In the art gallery we look at the carriage window through which we look out at the white horse etched in the hillside before it gallops away. Ah, those old compartment carriages and the Hitchcock plot-lines prowling up and down the corridor as we cross the Forth Bridge. In the hotel overlooking the bay the registrar balks at the word 'God' in a Wallace Stevens poem, pagan though he was, the line being 'We say God and the imagination are one'. We print and keep no photographs of the event. Often what marriage means on the daily level might be something on a utility bill in need of attention – no, that's a surname, we have different names – that kind of thing. Often in the shop I will be you or you be me depending on who is carrying whose ATM card. But then other bits and pieces of us come free in other ways too. This is my side of the bed, I will announce of a bed we have never slept in, because of a pattern carried here from our own bed at home. In the morning we wear each other's face, I mean farce. Hats I notice are neither mine nor yours, they are the property of whoever happens to pick them up. And now this goes for the children too. The who? The two-year-old takes the fifty-year-old's hat and puts it on. It fits just fine. But they are not here yet and I am getting ahead of myself. When the train approaches the tunnel I close my eyes and think myself forward into the light. Do you, I ask myself, visualise our forward motion in the same way. What is your sense of the distance until the next stop. In the station when we get home, the longest journey listed is to Penzance, for which a thirteen-hour train departs every morning. Living in their cottage in Cornwall, W. S. Graham would sit up writing his poetry in their tiny bedroom while his wife Nessie slept. There is a photograph of him doing just this, taken I presume on a timer. 'I leave this at your ear for when you wake.' Graham too had his journeys. Though resident in a small village with its one local pub, Graham chose to do his drinking in another village five or six miles away, walking home drunk in the dark. Sometimes he would get all the way home only to fall asleep in the garden. I write this in the dark with you in the next room, a long train journey away, it feels, while the moment holds, and with station name after name queued up to flash past, soon, unseen in my sleep.

§ 35

Swivel and pitch at the dump. Into the skip go the stairguard and plastic buggy. I develop a knack as I stand here emptying the car. One plastic bag I noticed was full of old *TLS*s, which I briefly attempt to check as they whizz past. Shouldn't I be cutting that review out and slipping it between the pages of a slim volume? Maybe not. Trickle of ochre juice at the bottom of the sack, dislodged as I throw and splattered now down my trouser leg. In Bohumil Hrabal's *Too Loud a Solitude* a man spends decades retrieving books from the dump where he works and studying them, acquiring a kind of PhD from the university of waste. And in fact some binmen in Turkey have just opened a library based on the books they pick up on their collections. On my demise my books will be scattered, make their way to the local charity shops among whose shuffling pensioners I rummage these days for children's games, for the bits of tat I end up feeding into the skip here. Commodious vicus of – the lifting and throwing done mainly by householders, while the dump workers sit in their hi-viz jackets on deckchairs – recirculation. In the previous country I stood feeding rubbish into a hatch and became aware of a CD of Glenn Gould playing Beethoven slipping through my fingers. Then gone. The last three Beethoven sonatas. I am not so uncritical a fan of Glenn Gould that I can't call his version of Op. 109 vaguely laughable, with its madly *prestissimo* tempo. Perhaps he did it to provoke. I could always replace the CD, and still feel twinges on that score, years later, but no doubt the performance is available on Youtube. So perhaps best not to let it play on the mind. Another time I went to the dump with the car and fed into the crusher, of all things, the car. So long, car, I said, slipping a smelly toy Bagpuss into my pocket. How small does the car get after crushing, though, the size of a table, the size of a suitcase. The area round the crusher was covered in spikes and baffles. Otherwise scavengers come for any old bits of copper or steel, and have been known to climb on the wrecks and even inside the machine. Waste not sent to landfill will often end up piled high on container ships bound for Africa or India. Are we at the stage yet of firing our waste into space, are other civilisations at the stage of firing theirs at us? One much-used feature of the abandoned car was its tape deck, which one does not find on more recent models. In the glove compartment was a whole library of mix tapes. Even today, this or that song is, to me, this-or-that-track-from-that-playlist-on-that-tape; they are forever clumped together thus in memory. And then the silences between tracks, the small whirr and click when the engine is ticking over at a light and the tape switches sides before – wait for it – another silence telling me what it is I'm about to hear.

§ 36

Just as my house is built on shifting foundations, my time here runs into the sand and I leave. Or do I mean mud, given the ubiquity of that element by the river, and do I mean pulls out of the mud, since I am leaving. I rummage around in a large and windowless cardboard-box shop in the east, less-favoured side of the city. Here my workplace and its satellite cafes and the occasional art gallery are distant rumours. Continuing my rambles further I pass the prison and see a sign for a visitors' centre and go in. Not that kind of visitors' centre, I learn. My mistake. A student of mine has worked here, and I ask him whether he's ever witnessed any skulduggery; several years previously Britain's longest-serving prisoner kidnapped a tutor and demanded an escape helicopter before he'd release him. His plan had been to fly to Cuba and have a beard-measuring competition with Fidel Castro. You do see things, my student tells me. Then they notice you've seen them and let it be known what will happen if you tell. That's how it works. A bar beside the prison, The Sportsman (that name again), features as a watering hole for prison officers in Robert Edric's thrillers. Surely this would cause tension with prisoners' family members, who would also drink there, I think. My friend Mike confirmed this, but told me people got one over on prison officers by reporting them for drink-driving when they left in an overly-refreshed condition. The Sportsman is a music venue, and among the bands playing there are The Penetrators, two of whose members are siblings of Trevor Bolder, bassist in David Bowie's Spiders from Mars alongside his fellow local guitar legend Mick Ronson. While on tour with the 'Cybernauts' Trevor Bolder painted his face blue but then discovered the paint was semi-permanent and would not come off: 'Bolder had to sell his car to raise the money needed for a specialist skin peeling process at a Swiss clinic', I read; 'to this day he still has traces of blue paint behind his left ear.' But I am leaving. The barman in The Sportsman presents the woman beside me with the pub telephone (landline). It is a child asking where she can find a pound coin. The leccy has gone off. She needs it to put the lights back on. Apologies once again for the frequently bar-themed nature of these anecdotes. Think nothing of it. I fill up the house with the cardboard boxes. My parents come over and help us pack. Once we have left, my parents go home too, then, strangely, return to the empty house and stay there a little bit longer. A house is more than mortar and bricks. You left a pair of shoes behind, my mother says, should I send them on. My house and its dirt on my shoes. No. Bin them, somebody else's rubbish now, and go.

§ 37

We drive eight hours north and finally see lit towers looming beyond the broad abundant sprawl of the valleys. 'Ye may gang far and fare waur' on the motorway services sign, scones (short 'o' here please), and pancakes made of bread. Tartan curtains where hauliers sleep in the slipstream of the traffic's rumble, then when their engines restart that moment when their trailers rein them back before they resettle and go on their way. I steer by the bright red T's of Tennents signs outside pubs, the city's one reliable winter primary colour. There are eyes in the stone, winking eyes, a 'glitter of mica at windy corners'. It is the guts of December, when shopping trolleys blow across the Tesco forecourt. Steps off the city-centre's long straight thoroughfare descend to a cobbled underpass running all the way down to the sea before more, sheer stone steps re-ascend, a fisherman's knot pulled tight round the streets. The union of Union Street is a workhouse, here are its barred-up windows admitting and releasing no light. Off the docks is an archway three feet high, a hobbit entrance for sailors jumping the wall for a night on the town. I have come to collect that glitter behind the stone, to pocket it like silver coins found on the pavement. Bright orange Arctic boats line up in the harbour, seemingly inches apart. The trick is to know just how to wedge yourself in. When the boats returned from Gothenburg, Alec Ferguson stood on the docks and welcomed everyone home, shaking their hands. At night the football stadium looks back to the sea like a monstrous washed-up skull, biting on nothing. Coming here on a train with no connections from Penzance, W. S. Graham composed an impromptu poem on the longest bar counter in the country, the line of drinks stretching away out of sight. Reunite it with itself over a Doom Bar. Wow wow, so you have returned at last, it says to itself. When I exit the bubble of whisky-warmed banter to drift home I am alone, with only the needle to the lungs of that killing sea breeze. Behind the long climb on the airport road sleep secret villages, slotted into the contours of the rivers down from the hills. Soon I will know them intimately who as yet do not so much as know their names. First though this house in a field with its thick walls and on-off relationship with the power supply. Are you there, are you sleeping, Nessie. I leave this at your ear for when you wake. Deer come to the garden, something or other leaves puncture marks in our cats' rear ends. One night I part a lace curtain and see the liverish-green drench of the merry dancers, the northern lights, in the far low corner of the sky. When you reach in the dark, in your sleep, for proof I am here, what do you find, who or what answers your touch while the frost coats the window and the candle left lighting gutters out in a mess of waxy collapse.

§ 38

Once and once only do I return from this place to the one immediately before it, as though all returns must involve the place of origin and no other. My colleague has died. I am struck in travelling by the rickety griminess of the train, not that I remember much luxury before, but this seems a new level of studied neglect. *Bummelzug*, is the term I believe in German. A man opposite me is shaving himself where he sits, little sprays of his chin-hair landing at his feet where he has angled himself out into the aisle. In all my journeys has there been an implied straight line between the points of setting out and arrival – or eventual straight line, once all the false starts and circlings back have been accounted for? Let us hope not. Or do I revisit only, in some paradox of the time-traveller, to rub out all traces of my having ever been here, if I am really here at all? Then as chance would have it I read in the train of how the former local poet too has been revisiting, death notwithstanding. In later life he was rather deaf, and his hearing-aid manufacturer was a member of a spiritualist group with unusual beliefs in how the dead contact the living, involving, as in Beckett's *Krapp's Last Tape*, the tape-recorder. The machine would be left to record in silence, and when played back the cassette would contain messages from the beyond. In this way the poet could still be reached. What are you doing now, he was asked. Tramping, came the answer, tramping. I am struck again by the importance of technology in my relationship with time. Tape recorders are now rather quaint contraptions, and it seems unreasonable of the dead to bind us to that medium, however much in their nostalgia they might wish to cling to it. In reality, or in ghost fiction at least, the dead are more likely to stay up to date, spoiling our fun with mobile phones and emails by sending us untraceable missives on every new medium they can find. I remember my grandmother, who was rather deaf too, getting a hearing aid but preferring not to turn it on. When she did it would often emit loud squawks of feedback, as though an angry hornet had turned up to halt the conversation. I remember too my first mobile phones, dead and unhauntable now, off in their distant drawers or landfills. The same drawers once maintained lovingly, forgetfully, in my house here and which, inspected before I left, I found full of floppy disks and their urgently unreadable testimonies. Returning to the dead poet's library I open a book and an acquisition slip signed by the poet himself falls out. The book has never been opened or read. Are you there though, I ask, do you have something to say. Shifting awkwardly in my coat on the train I find the phone in my trousers pocket has turned on its camera and started recording. There is a low rumble of motion from the train but not much by way of spirit activity. Unless the ghost is me. Can a ghost haunt itself? Give it up. Give up what. What does a ghost. Giving up. Give up.

§ 39

I have often wondered what language it is I speak. I hear a rumble of conversation in Gaelic outside my office and before stepping outside look up the word for photocopier. *Lethbhreacadair. Tha an lethbhreacadair air a bhriseadh a-rithist.* It's broken again. It certainly is. I enter the post office and am aware of some avian commotion outside on the footpath. The mither and faither are greetin fer the bairnie craw, someone in the queue ahead of me reports, the mother and father are weeping for the baby crow. A language is a dialect with a navy. Where is your navy. A paper fifie fleetin oan the Don, a paper boat on the river behind the Co-op. Writing an essay on whether there had been a Scottish literature, T. S. Eliot decided there was, briefly, but hadn't been for some centuries. It lacks the 'continuity of the language'; it is a provincial literature. 'Aesthetic agitation' has been known to occur in 'the Highland brain', but this phenomenon keeps itself to itself. He was responding to a writer, one G. Gregory Smith, who had coined the phrase 'the Caledonian anti-syzygy' to describe the warring contraries that make up the Scottish condition. To Smith, the absence of the settled identity Eliot finds in England is an opportunity, and makes Scotland the distinctive entity it is. To Eliot, it just means incoherent provincialism. Writing his great poems in Scots, Hugh MacDiarmid draws heavily on Jamieson's *Etymological Dictionary of the Scottish Language*. When composing the lovely 'Water Music', MacDiarmid has access to the first of its two volumes but not the second; hence the preponderance in that poem of Scots words beginning with letters from the first half of the dictionary. Is this true. Let me look into it. Later

MacDiarmid becomes infuriated by the young Ian Hamilton Finlay's poems in Glaswegian, which MacDiarmid considers the language of the gutter. Strange disconnection. I write as I speak. In the company of my old Irish teacher I noticed he addressed his wife in Irish and she answered in English. He was in the habit of filling the blackboard, at school, with cascades of plot paraphrases of the short stories we were studying, and which we were required to commit to memory. But so quickly did he write that he often erased the text before we had properly copied it down, rendering the whole exercise impossible and absurd. In this sense too he was once again speaking only to himself. Brushing up on my Irish I watch a video of a young Nigerian-born Irishwoman discussing, in Irish, black women's hair. All too predictably she has received racial abuse from people who suggest she has no 'genetic connection' to the language. The purchase of a Rolex watch is an expression of choice and agency people feel able to grasp. The speaking of a minority language less so, for some reason. In the Nigerian-born Irishwoman's case, less so again. Why would anyone do this. Where is Wuraola Majekodunmi's navy, they must ask themselves. Enough, *is leor sin*. The river Don is not really navigable, even by paper boats. I have tried it. You launch the boat and realise in the same instant you have no idea where it is going to end up.

§ 40

Surrounded by castles as I am, I find myself roaming over the centuries by way of the strange assembly of portraits that hang on their walls. Contemporary or twentieth-century portraits are, I decide, null, to be disregarded with summary indifference. These leftovers of a cancelled class might hold out in a corner of their properties, battling a leaky roof and the internal revenue, but their memorialisation in garish oils comes pre-forgotten. Victorian portraits have a bit more swagger to them, with their kitsch highland accoutrements and moustachioed eminences fresh from Sudan or Rajasthan. But these too hold little appeal. Now, the eighteenth century, that was something. Here is a beefy and perruqued laird who has chosen the wrong side in the Jacobite risings and suffered dispossession and imprisonment, before somehow contriving to return. That's the spirit. But it is a portrait from the previous century where I spot what I realise I have been seeking. Much smaller than recent canvases, it hangs high in a corner above a door, ignored, I imagine, by most of the visitors who file aimlessly under it, and features a rakish, anonymous soldier, emerging from a dark background but with the smallest tincture of purple to the shine on his armour. A Virgilian purple, I decide, carried over from a more heroic age. Looking at it closely I fancy I see the painter's face reflected somewhere in its sheen. Looking at it more closely again I fancy I see my own, somehow inside the canvas now and taking my measure from this sturdy gallowglass. Which side has he been on in the endless wars of that age, I wonder. In the War of Three Kingdoms, for instance, were he alive for that, when Irish soldiers fought in

Scotland for an English king against Scottish Presbyterians, am I getting that right. I think again of the Earl of Montrose, a Covenanter himself before a conversion to Catholicism and a traumatic switching of sides. He never fights the English and is thus spared the facile myth-spinning that overtook Wallace and the Bruce. I sense he is dimly remembered now, if not by demented fossickers and memorialists such as I. But that shade of purple: I see it again in the tartan shawl in the giftshop in the courtyard. In the line of heather on the mountain above the line of trees on the approach to the castle. On a jay's feather on my path on a walk through the woods. In the kitsch suit of armour standing guard in the lobby of a small country hotel. Skimmed from that spot on the colour palette where grey, brown and blue mix and combust into what I decide is the colour of history, that precise, knowing episcopal shade, the glint in the eye of a nameless cavalier inspected in the gloom of a late autumn afternoon in an empty Scottish castle. And it is there too in the greeny-grey of my wife's eye as she turns over, staring at me semi-awake on the pillow, the image of my quizzical face just visible on the small meniscus of her pupil.

§ 41

The poverty of their family portraits may give the impression
that by the twentieth century these castles have shrunk to
National Trust-supported relics, in the larger scheme of things.
Not always so. Thus: the Alvis slowed to a crawl along the
potholed road easily and parked in the lee of the pink-harled
castle. It was Ramsay, come from the club meeting. He had
spoken for hours without notes, to warm applause. The grip of
the moneylenders on public life was now absolute, he had told
them. Their hidden hand controls the press, the parliament,
and the crown itself. But what of the sheepfarmers of the Moor-
foots, the man from the *Peebleshire Advertiser* had asked. They
too shall be made free men again. He ended with his time-hon-
oured rallying cry: perish Judah! The Duke of Wellington had
taken the chair and here he was with Ramsay at the castle
to advance their plans. The campaign against the anti-Christ
would continue. By means of a small camera easily stored in
an inside jacket pocket the blueprints could be photographed
and the images passed to the ambassador in a cigar box. The
files and the members' ledger were stored in the compartment
behind the bookcase, far from the Argus eyes of the enemy.
When the baron rang the operator and asked to be put through
to the embassy, he was aware of a click on the line. And will
you be attending the vintage car fête, he asked, making small
talk while he waited. They are a simple folk when uncontami-
nated. Ramsay would spend the war in prison while the baron
remained at large to continue his work for the cause. In his last
years, Ramsay worked on *The Nameless War*, a work of deranged
anti-Semitism. The execution of Charles I had been staged by

Cromwell's Jewish backers for the purposes of readmitting the Jews to Britain. It seems history is to blame. And now a man is at the door canvassing for the local elections. Am I concerned about dog poo on the paths, he wants to know, people have strong views about it, I've found. He has strong views on the withholding of council tax from our communist government, who are nevertheless ethno-nationalists too. Hints of a larger madness in the air. How to process it. Under Godwin's law any invocation of Hitler means the argument is over. Seems sensible. It's in poor taste. In a sensible world. Do not compare current unravellings to those of the past. The tatty old flag flew over the town hall for the Duke of York's birthday, the slaver's statue floated like a stylite in an amnesiac cloud on his pillar. Seems normal. Do not question the discourse. I have made my position on that issue perfectly clear, the man on the doorstep continues, but I suppose you can't say anything these days without. They're hardly sending their brightest and best. 'Speak English, dog' (Tom Raworth). It's not racialist, property values go down when that happens and that's just a fact. If you dislike it so much you can always. But then anything I say seems to annoy them. Annoy you. Fine. Why are you so always so. Angry. You. You people.

§ 42

The upstairs of the country hotel is arranged like a courtyard, and sitting where I do I enjoy a view of the small swimming pool and the grand pianos and ample sofas below. A waist-coated hotel worker comes and goes among innumerable prints of highland pursuits, all Tam-o'shantered ghillies and blank-eyed Victorians pursuing their bloodlust across the moors. Fellow mid-morning coffee drinkers are scattered around, some doing what looks like work, involving scattered papers and multiple open tabs on their laptops, as just about visible to you above the pages of your book. A couple in dressing gowns flop with their cocktails onto a sofa, post-swim. The hotel is just off the A96, up and down which commuters alternate between their satellite towns and city workplaces, but efforts have been made here to suggest a Highlands bolthole away from all that. Would I care to see the whisky list? This one has a sweet nose, whereas this one is peaty, and this one has a citrus aftertaste. Suddenly the hotel is mobile, and I transplant it to the shores of a loch somewhere in the shadow of a large Cairngorms peak. An unspeakable hunting party has returned and is noisily reliving its exploits in a nearby corner. I have felt the need for a third Scotch to get me past the halfway mark in my Walter Scott novel, while I mentally reel off the names of the mountain corries and lochs over the ridge of the mountain visible through the bay window. And I am close, close to where I need to be, tucked into a fold on the map, and able to skip suddenly from one environment, one century, one language, to another. But I do this first of all by skipping from one version of this hotel armchair to another, merely by shifting from haunch to haunch and rubbing my eyes behind my glasses. There is a line of trees through the bay window, but beyond them is commuter traffic and a market town, confirmation of how wilful the transformations are that I am working. But with just that little effort the magic works and it has all led to this point, from the village on the reservoir in the mountains of my homeland to the metallic echoes of the car ferry to the cat down a tenfoot and now this. And what brought you here, I ask the Romanian waiter who has asked me about my novel, and soon we fall into conversation about writers from his homeland. He explains about the course he is taking at the university, but no, I feel like saying, I meant what roads to villages on reservoirs, what dog down a side-street, what track to an empty house after an eight-hour drive has he followed; I mean not the purpose of the journey but the journey itself. But his journey has continued in search of our coffee and he is gone.

§ 43

In the village, a statue of James Mitchell, 'carrier'. Every day
in Victorian times, I learn, he hauls a wagon the sixteen miles
from the village to the city, distributing and collecting despite
post his not being able to read. Perhaps he has evolved a system
of mnemonics to help him with his deliveries. I trace the route
on my ordnance survey map, and think how mundane it must
have been for people to tramp sixteen miles between village
and city then, and how long it must be since anyone attempted
such a journey now. And why would they? But then I realise I
am not tracing the route or anything like it, and that Mitchell
might have taken a right at the roundabout to strike out over
this field, that burn, this hill . . . He slashes and whacks at the
banks of nettles with his blackthorn and pauses to remove a
stone from a shoe. He breaks into a canter coming down an
incline only to lose a wheel. And what name would you have
on the recumbent by the edge of the wood, I might ask him, I
mean in the forest clearing, the clearing in the Victorian forest
I now find myself in. But then the city itself is much altered
too, it strikes me, as we reach the tanner's yard and the coaching inn on its outskirts. People are quicker to salute, I note,
acknowledging the doffed cap of a passing whiskered minister.
You I know, I observe to a crescent row of granite townhouses,
though lacking their satellite dishes and parking meters. I see
people don't wear hats anymore, Mitchell for his part observes,
not happy with the bus behind us sounding its horn, and needing reassurance from me on the low-flying planes overhead.
Our time zones appear to have merged, mixter-maxter. And
what's this one, I ask of a clarty sack in the cart tied with a

shoelace. Twa poond o' neeps fer the meenister inby Hard-weird. On another occasion I have found myself travelling in the opposite direction, waiting at the stand for the last bus back to the village only to learn it had departed from elsewhere in the station without an announcement. Come on then, a driver told me, and we boarded a second bus to chase the first. We got right to the top of Tyrebagger before catching up and, sig-nalling wildly, persuaded the empty first bus to pull in. I had not expected to find myself walking, however briefly, along the dual carriageway this far out so late at night. But one journey will often turn into another. Time and space change mid-jour-ney, taking me somewhere other than where I had thought, by a different route, arriving years before or after I set out, the name on the letter in our hands having changed as we walked. When my child was a newborn and needed an early morning nap on the sofa, the postman would instinctively know not to ring the bell for a parcel, but slip the front door open, place the parcel inside, and close the door again noiselessly as he went on his way.

§ 44

Squeak of James Mitchell, carrier's, wagon wheels again over
his desire path across the rough field, while I sit in the window
of a corporate coffee chain on the A96. On the A96 as the
lorries go past and the yellow caterpillar of morning headlights
noses endlessly past the red caterpillar going in the other direction. The satisfying thrum of the traffic pulsing through the
floor as I hunch over my corporate coffee. The road goes down
and the road goes up, the morning planes go over, to a noise
not unlike the coffee machine reaching its urgent crescendo
in the corner. A noise I might normally consider insufferable,
and yet here I am. Why is that. It is the promise of its transport to another realm, a becinnamoned elsewhere, signposted
by the foamy vortex swirl atop your oversized mug. Than the
absence of which, which happens, which has been known to
happen, there is no greater small disaster, of a morning – no
greater disaster than receiving the mug sans foam and thinking, what's this, and having that moment in which to speak or
do nothing, and doing nothing, how can the day recover. But
thankfully not on this occasion. The mechanics of the coffee's
slow slither down the edges, the wraiths and wreaths it leaves
in its wake. Why is it, I wonder, the servers behind the counter
communicate through earpieces despite standing several feet
apart. Because they too have entered into the ceremony of the
occasion, call that ceremony, yes, yes, I do. In the corner booth
an affecting scene plays out over two untouched drinks. A
woman in a business suit cries suffocatedly while the man, also
in a suit and a lanyard round his neck, leans over periodically
to touch her hand before sliding back across the sizable table.

What's going on. Furtive glance at his watch. Get it over with now and slink off to work. Unless she will be doing the same thing. Perhaps at the Downhole Products office down the way. For all your downhole needs. Anyone want a coffee, someone will ask mid-morning. You two, you look like you need one. Then go along with it rather than have to explain yourself, the hateful beverage poured down a sink or into a plant and the styrofoam cup left on a shelf and forgotten. I will proceed down the road to my workplace, and make good time. But what to do when I arrive early at the huge slab-like building, where I will climb to the seventh floor and stare out over the sea and pin-wheel turbines striding all the way to Norway. What but purchase another coffee and start again, standing in the queue while the coffee machine reaches its urgent crescendo again in the corner. A noise I might normally consider insufferable, and yet here I am. Why is that. Could it be the promise of transport to another realm, a becinnamoned elsewhere. But we had that before. Transported where. Am I not still here. Do I go and slip back again, not noticing. Where am I now. The trawlers thread their way between the turbines and loud and boisterous grows the wind and loud and stormy grows the sea.

§ 45

Mornings then I find myself in one of those rooms, whether looking out over the battleship-grey winter sea, with off in the distance the football stadium and the pier, or down into the courtyard, and talk to whoever comes in the door, that small knot somewhere in my eyeline, not many, while I talk, as follows. Perhaps you are familiar with Bach's preludes and fugues, I might start. Let me describe for you a technique he uses called stretto, and off we go, with me silently tapping out the melodies on the desk as I spoke. G – E flat – F – G . . ., what must they have made of that. Time, I would say, time moves now fast, now slowly, sometimes both at once, how is that. Soon after Bach's death he fell out of fashion. Fashions change, but there is also the question of the thing itself, the 'ghostlier demarcations, keener sounds', having to move on, and find their next form. *The forms are many in which the formless seeks relief from the unchanging.* If we skip forward to the twentieth century, we find Schoenberg – Schoenberg, I hope you know Schoenberg – floundering in the backwash from late Romanticism. Floundering in some style, but in need of something or other to happen, to pull away from that aporia. Yet for all the thrill of what did happen next, Schoenberg always presented himself as a reluctant radical, even as people responded to his work by throwing chairs. Is this not peculiar, to fancy yourself merely the medium through which the statement of your art is made, whatever you might feel about it personally – Adam, of what are you the medium? Are we the medium not just of our art, but of our daily lives? Do we sit here talking or are we the vehicles of that sitting? But I'm rambling. Or am I the vehicle of my rambling? It goes against nature, people thought, *Pierrot Lunaire* and its cackling shrieks. No one ever hummed along to a tune like that. But I am that person, I hum along to these tunes. Adam, you can sing, could you do some *Sprechstimme* for us? To some, Yankee Doodle is a naturally-occurring melodic phenomenon but Schoenberg's String Trio is not, is a perversion, a stunt, a game. But what do we think? Schoenberg wrote his String Trio after having died on the operating table and being brought back to life by a needle through the heart. This music is that needle. If it's a game, the stakes are quite high. But there is that question of artistic control, of form and method bringing those elements under control. Among Schoenberg's followers, there was a sense that if melody could be organised like this, then why not other elements too, like rhythm. It was a heroic time, that post-war period, and when I hear a piece like Ligeti's *Atmosphères*, to add that to the mix, I feel as though some giant UFO has flown into place above my head, and is hovering there, mysteriously. What does it want from me? I should also mention that Ligeti's music is very funny, even at is most controlled. But why stop there, others thought, wherever 'there' is. If we achieve maximal artistic control only to cause maximal audience confusion, or alarm, have we not reached a point where freeplay and improvisation have become possible again, almost without anyone noticing? Or so John Cage thought. You can push through that tunnel and emerge back into the light. A hand on the window. A wave on the shore. I think there is light. If you push at the window and open to listen and see. I think there is light.

§ 46

It might seem odd to talk about politics in a discussion of harmony, rhythm and string quartets. Think of it here as a backdrop of a larger reality, the chambers of the communal ear listening in as we play. But when we go through that tunnel I mentioned, strange things start to happen. Another late modernist composer, Cornelius Cardew, saw and seized that freedom I described. He wrote pieces whose scores don't have any notes. If you look at *Treatise*, it's more like a graphic novel – *The Adventures of the Very Large Black Circle*, perhaps. You might stare at it and think, what is this stuff. And that's an understandable reaction. And then if you look it up, you'll find performances of it executed in that spirit of radical improvisation. Unsurprisingly, they're in what we might call the plink-plonk-crash-bang-wallop style (which I love), with their tragic little fronds and feints of broken lines sent out into the vacuum, the void. But something happened to Cardew. He became a Maoist and decided his modernist music was incompatible with the class struggle. He published a book about his old teacher called *Stockhausen Serves Imperialism*. He changed his style and started composing in a ploddingly obvious diatonic style, in pieces like 'Revolution Is the Main Trend'. You can still buy the scores of these later pieces from the online shop of the Revolutionary Communist Party of Great Britain. It's worth pointing out that this new direction didn't make his work any more popular than his previous stuff. Then he died young. Maybe he would have changed his style again had he lived. Maybe not. But here is a contrast for you. His Italian contemporary Luigi Nono was also an avant-garde diehard. Unlike Cardew though, he saw a radical avant-garde style as precisely the vehicle he needed for his politics. There is a piece of his called *Il Canto Sospeso*, whose vocal score is based on the final letters of resistance fighters before their execution by the Nazis. The Italian Communist Party was more of a force in politics than Cardew's outfit were, so maybe that helped. But then if you listen to a piece like *La Lontananza Nostalgica Utopica Futura* (whose title is so wonderful, is it not), written in the late 80s, you have a piece that feels like handling broken glass or barbed wire, a piece that positively glowers and fumes and crackles. But what's on its mind. It's about distance, our nostalgic distance from the past, but a past from which the future used to be visible. It would be a brave listener who decided this was a case of self-seducing highbrow melancholy, the avant-garde lounging on its chaise longue at the Grand Hotel Abyss. No. You attend a performance. Ten music stands are dispersed around an empty stage. What are we waiting for? Music begins to play, but on a tape. A solitary violinist comes on stage. He moves around, stepping into the audience, playing from now this score, now that. A technician controls the pre-recorded tracks, turning them up full-blast or off altogether. We wander bewildered through a graveyard of possibilities and the graves spring open, empty, and we are their walking corpses, sent relentlessly on our way, not knowing where that might be.

§ 47

As I may have established by now, I am easily disoriented, and emerging from watching a roomful of students take an exam I find myself not in the corridor by which I had entered the room, but a featureless alcove, sunk a few steps below floor-level. How has that happened. Directly under a distant sky-light is a solitary chair, whose dowdy aspect is enough to catch my fancy and stop me turning on my heels, for a moment at least. A good chair on which to sit uncomfortably in some pebble-dashed hospital out-building and wait for a doctor to enter and break the news of my test results, the terrible news. The building in which I am in fact wandering dates from a brief Cromwellian invasion of the city during the War of the Three Kingdoms in the 1640s, in the course of which Catholics from my homeland allied with Anglicans from down there to fight Presbyterians from up here, am I getting that right. If I gaze out the bathroom window, in another of its creaking alcoves, I enjoy oblique views of the chapel, with its distinctive closed crown. I am looking out over rooftops from this small upper-storey window and wait to hear again the boats and the gulls I heard long ago in the music college. (Pause for breath.) I also enjoy the large unwieldy wooden doors and the general air of good-humoured desuetude: a large missing patch of wall-plaster here, some indecipherable chalk scribbles on an old blackboard there, but only in the dusty embrace of this oubli-ette do I feel my sense of enclosure become complete. Left in the centre of the floor, the chair, that chair again, stands ready to lend itself to the needs of any passing interrogators. Have you consorted with Royalists?, a fearsome Covenanter might want to ask. Have you broken bread with the enemies of Christ and the Republic?' For two hours I have alternated between a Thomas Bernhard novel and glances at the rows of quizzical Italians, Germans and Norwegians, wondering how they were adjusting to their new surroundings. I think of the city as the far north, but perhaps for the Scandinavians the reference points are inverted, and they see themselves as visiting a balmy south, for all that I think of that useful local word 'dreich' as an omni-purpose descriptor of the city where I work. I walk up the steps and see, out the window again, the students emerge from the building and disperse round the chapel. From next year, the visiting students' exam will be completed online, and visits here, though in no sense ruled out, will become haphazard, subject to unknown whims and random political disasters. 'You spent many years there', some future interrogator will ask me, who knows when and where, 'is there anything about that time you wish to record?' Yes, there was a small sunken room with a chair and a skylight, near the top of a tower.

§ 48

While we live a short distance from the mountains and highlands proper, our region is not, in itself, any kind of established
tourist draw. I therefore wonder about the caravan parks I see
dotted round the place. Here down a side road is a huddle of
caravans with their quaint lace curtains and rows of trinkets in
the windows. We're some distance from the village and there
are no on-site facilities. Nevertheless, for some hardy campers,
this is the place to be. A long novel on a short day and a clinking shopping bag's worth of cabin fuel: would that help? But
then I happen upon an abandoned caravan park and see where
these dreams come to grief. Collapse is a gradual, asynchro-
nous thing. A flimsy balsa-wood door has come off its hinges
and the floor has collapsed. But here are the plates in the sink,
needing only a bit of a scrape. A sofa endures, offers its tattered
arm for a spot of perching, and I am happy to oblige. Large
portions of walls are missing, but in a randomly chewed-off
manner, like those east-coast cliffs falling into the sea. I have
been reading a friend's novel set in an abandoned housing
estate and think, what is this, is someone taking the mickey,
is that someone me. And here at the edge of the caravan park
is an occupied static home, lights on. It is the owner. There
has been a dispute and the business has been wound up, but
she's not moving. These are perfectly good sites. People will
always need static homes. People will always need psychiatric
hospitals. Just down the road crouches a large turreted hospital behind a security fence, multiply breached and admitting
me to a vast ballroom, lit by a row of stained-glass windows
over the balustrade on a nearby balcony. It may not be prudent

to continue. Quantities of discarded files lie in bundles on the floor. Dosages administered, columns and columns of them, sheet music and drawings, a Victorian volume fallen open on its title page – *Episodes from the Early Life of a Scottish Public Health Officer.* Is that piano in tune. Some strings and hammers missing, in some cases correspondingly so. There is evidence of a system of security doors down the corridor, securing the wards (cells?) further off. But how can we help you. Have you been having those thoughts again. Come through this door. Notice how imperceptibly it seals behind you. If it helps you should think of it as less an illness than a condition. Writing materials will be provided. Some people are morbidly drawn to abandoned spaces. The world will always need ruins. But we are here to work. Concentrate. Start at the start. Press this buzzer for help. It's a secluded spot. Often the sun will not get very much higher than the line of pine trees outside. But wait long enough in the ballroom and a rainbow spotlight will fall. You may even find, if you have been paying attention, that you have been standing in one all along.

§ 49

The piano tuner is a blind man, Mr Worcester. You were on *Countdown*, weren't you, I mention, passing him a cup of tea, what was it like. They had excellent biscuits. He rocks back and forth as he eats, smiling broadly. As a blind man you must get asked a lot of stupid questions, I think, without saying. When I smile I am often aware of doing so to defuse people, so they'll leave me alone. Reciprocal acknowledgement and then pass, good to go. For whom does the tuner smile. Himself. Tidy whack of a tuning fork on wood and, C, middle C! D! E! The piano tuner is the first ever person to whom I have mentioned a Pythagorean comma who knows what I'm talking about. The Pythagorean comma designates a discrepancy in the tuning of the chromatic scale. Twelve fifths on a piano are equivalent to seven octaves, but in reality these two measures are not the same. A small gap opens up between them, and if the tuning reflected this the piano would sound off, to our ears. We solve the problem by flattening the octaves ever so slightly, closing the gap. If I didn't pin the notes down, the tuner says, the notes would all float off, in the ether, then where would we be. Banjaxed! Do you play yourself, I ask. Yes, but only when no one is listening. Are you familiar with scrooping. It's that little rattle you hear behind the note, the ghost of a squeak. We'll soon get that seen to. While he works the cat has crept up and tucked herself under the keyboard, by the piano leg, listening while the vibrations pass through her body, running them to earth. The tuner's telephone speaks as he works, like the most tactful of butlers, always to hand. Yes, a bottle of red with lunch when I'm back, won't be long. 'Bessie' the Bechstein is proving recalcitrant! But we'll see her right. You build up a map in your head, he says, of the blindness. If I was off to the shop but went the wrong way I'd know from the footpath, instinctively. You know when you're on the road you want and then when you're not. Does that sound fanciful. And do you play yourself. Yes, but more with expression than accuracy. In the car as I drive him home I notice his fingers playing scales on his knees: 'Heard melodies are sweet but those unheard.' Music is a performance but also an idea. Sounds abstract. Not necessarily. When he wrote *Art of the Fugue* Bach did not indicate any instruments. Why. Was it all just in his head by then. But Beethoven never heard the late quartets. Some things lie off the spectrum, the whistle at the end of *Sergeant Pepper* that made dogs bark. Those are scales aren't they, I observe, I saw you putting your thumb under after three notes. Got to keep your technique in trim, he replies. Otherwise how are you ever going manage the really hard stuff. On the keyboard or your knee? Oh, so silence isn't enough for you then?! Excuse *me* [laughs]!

§ 50

There in the dark and waiting. One then the other. There was a flood in the park each time, make of this what you may. At the sowing of the seed. A warm bag the size of a mouse and growing. A mouse the size of a mouse and growing, its small veined sac a lidless eyeball, watching. We were halfway up a hill when a name came to us, as though waiting there under a stone. I know you're in there but can you come out now. A dream of putting my eye to a keyhole and finding behind it another keyhole to look through and so on and on, and you there waiting, at the end. An outside inside an inside, inside an outside, inverting my sense of space like a paper fortune-teller in my hand. Is there time to stop for coffee en route to the hospital, I wonder. Surprisingly yes. I stir the dregs and lick the spoon dry. In the hospital I notice the high, round windows and think of portholes. Endometriosis patients take the same corridors as patients for the maternity ward, then branch off. We're close, we are so close. Why are you holding that walrus figurine, asks a nurse. I like to carry it about my person, do you mind if I – its little head peeping out under my scrubs as I enter the theatre. When the child emerges they go up in the air in the nurse's arms before coming down into yours, then later mine, all to the sound of a cello. But like a stuck zip the cannula in your arm will not dislodge and the hospital becomes a labyrinth I prowl, awaiting release, an antiseptic liminal zone between the within and without, the sunlight glimpsed through the oil rig and William Wallace figures on the bed-curtains. A voice across the room whispers into a phone of how if they talk to the 'services' the nurses might come and take the bairn away. Smokers I see through the window gather outside by the no-smoking signs. Then one day we breeze down the corridor and away from the whole overlit clamjamfrie to a dark warm room. Begin again. You are lying on your back in the dark in a small warm room, tossing this way and that, moving between sleeps while a fugitive shadow passes over the wall behind you. A cat jumps on the bed and startles in her encounter with the heedless other, then beds down beside you, absorbing you into her circle of closed-eyed acceptance. And so we linger on that moment of unseeing emergence, that passage through the most decisive of portals only to spend our time prone in a shared dream and as though carried still within some larger womb-like envelope, posting ourselves to our future selves, for delivery soon, soon. Both of you, two years apart. I turn the key in the lock of these memories and climb into bed beside you again, waiting for first light to tear the envelope open, shake us awake and spill us back into ourselves.

§ 51

Far enough north for the view of the sea to include west and east simultaneously, the artist Ellis O'Connor looks out over the waves at a crucible of white, grey, black, brown, green and blue. The paint is dense, I see the swells and currents thrash on the small canvas on my wall, but also notice a small raised smudge on the canvas of hers that hangs there, as though a gnat had got caught in a brushstroke. When I look at O'Connor's paintings I will seek out a vanishing point, even when the lines appear to pile up randomly, pulling the gaze in every direction. I strain to see the painting in a more disassembled way, disabling the pull of the eye back towards the vanishing point and the perspectival frame. The gaze bobs in her paint like a buoy in the bay, tethered yet free. On the island where she paints a camera obscura hides inside a stone hut, inverting and reversing the events on the sea outside. The aperture will for preference be sphincter-tight and small. The camera obscura may have played a part in neolithic ceremonies, and helped reveal the unwatchable motions of solar eclipses. I sat inside it once waiting patiently for something to happen. A bird flies over and flies in the opposite direction inside my beehive cell. Or is it a smudge on the lens. But how does O'Connor paint her storms at sea. In any case soon her island homeland will be underwater, each incoming wave hissing its threat on the way in and out. She has painted Uist, Iceland, Svalbard, they could not be more different, they are all the same. Slowly I enter the dark and the silence under the wave and stay there long enough to consider them final, somewhere off beyond the plane of the feasible. Some years ago an artist was found in a bothy on Cape Wrath with a Woolworths bag stuffed with rubbish. She had stopped eating, believing she could subsist on colour and light, and died in a hospital shortly afterwards. She shares a name with a Victorian artist and collector, which makes tracing her own art rather difficult, if not impossible. The Wrath in Cape Wrath is not 'wrath'; it means 'turning point' in Old Norse. Eventually though you run out of north. If transported to the south of France would O'Connor stop painting, I wonder, powerless before its heat-maps of yellow, red and orange. Or would she enter that colourworld as easily as a sonata changes key. Yes and no, is that your answer to everything, yes and no. Is it the place or is it the glow she sees and paints that becomes the place. Many of the places she paints have never been seen. Even on the canvas, they still are not there. I gaze hard at the small raised smudge on her canvas which the artist herself may never have noticed. It becomes a turning point. My gaze rests on it and all the liquid in my eye drains down its plughole and away.

§ 52

Behind a row of flaming torches and under a peak in the middle distance still snowy in August the pipers march round the field, snaking and turning to the tune of 'The Boneshaker' and 'The Cameronian Rant'. I love the moment at the start of their performance when the shout goes out and the pipes groan into life, like a cat on the bed stretching her legs languidly before going tense again. The pipes are not an orchestral instrument (technically they are not an instrument at all but a weapon of war), and therefore their tuning system has gone its own eccentric way unchecked down the ages. Often they will be pitched halfway between B and B flat and tuned to between 476 and 480 Hz, where modern concert pitch is closer to 466 Hz. Maybe this is what gives the pipes the extra bite to their timbre, like the touch of frost in the air here in the eastern highlands. Historically pitch was not standardised, causing all kinds of problem for ensemble playing. With the invention of tuning forks and the drift towards standardisation, pitch began to creep upwards. It is evolution in action. But players of older music pine for the old tunings, the deeper echoing resonance of a viol da gamba played in the music room of a highlands castle. So if you have perfect pitch and can hear that note for an A, which A is it you're hearing: modern A, historical A, true A, which is which. I used the word 'authentic' but nowadays the term 'historically informed performance' is preferred. We can recreate a seventeenth-century instrument but not, I would have thought, seventeenth-century ears. If, that is, it is in the here and now that we listen and not across the centuries. But while old equals lower, in this debate, the pipes – an instrument out of time – confound that. Now a piper is playing on the battlements of a castle, while our children tense their arms and shake their fists with excitement. A lone piper playing the *piobaireachd* or *ceol mòr* will start with a slow movement, or *ùrlar*, before performing complex variations on it. These will include a *siubhal* ('passing'), with a proliferation of grace notes, and likewise the *dithis* ('pair'). Other movements follow, with names including the *leumluath*, *taorluath*, and *crùnluath*. By now we are far from the marches played by most pipe-bands and deep into the ceremonial-symbolic dimension of the music. It can be played for laments, for heroes lost in battle, for meetings between clan chiefs, or even on the occasion of stepping into a boat, with the piper occupying the stern and piping us across. At the D-Day landings a piper was ordered to march up and down on the beach and play under fire. The *ceol mòr* our piper is playing is 'Hector MacLean's Warning'. What is he warning us of, what should we do. But now each of the pipers in the field has started their own *ceol mòr*, marching up and down furiously in all directions as they play but without any collisions. Is it a *ceol mòr* of victory or defeat, of or arrival, or of our simply being here, a *ceol mòr* for the *ceol mòr* itself; the pipes, fantastical creatures that they are, are bearing down on us as they play, closer and closer, preparing the groans of terrible triumph they will expel when they fall on us at last.

§ 53

And then to find on the outskirts of the village a stump of Victorian railway line, a disappointed bridge flanking the road west. Many of these Victorian lines did little more than service their local lairds' back gardens, handy for shipping in oysters and claret. A novelty railway line survives in the next town. We chuff round its circuit, not very much faster than had we been walking. The child's hands stim, becoming the train that they ride. There are old railway mags in the transport museum café, I am pleased to discover. Ken and Barbara love their Barnsley diesels so much they decided to get married on one – and we were there! The miniature rail line closes shortly afterwards, but the child has caught its ghost train, goes on travelling the circular line round its damp field. Further into the highlands a station is surrounded by spaced-out mountains with in front of them greats bogs and moors. A man arrives and sets off up the biggest peak and does not come down. He has travelled from France in mysterious circumstances, as will emerge in time. It is the position of the body that seems somehow strange when he is found, perched on the edge of a cliff. In the absence of any identification, the dead man is given a placeholder name. In the 1740s an outlaw lived rough for years on the mountain slopes, as recorded in Stevenson's *Kidnapped*. The pistol found on the dead man's body is curiously antique. You have decided you will die, where will it happen. Stay where you are in your room and turn to the wall and what do you see. You face the blank wall and collide with that finality. So why travel so far, what do you hope to find, opening yourself to the extreme unknown and escaping into it. The man had emotional problems. There was an incident in his youth. He had been sacked from his job. He was involved with historical re-enactors. His bewildered parents receive unusual communications. The mountains had meant something to him, but what. MacPherson of Cluny, chief of the Clan MacPherson, led an itinerant existence while in hiding, taking great care to evade the redcoats. Although set in difficult and isolated terrain the railway station has achieved fame, of a slightly paradoxical kind, featuring in a television series on 'secret stations'. How secret if we know where it is. It is also the station featured at the beginning of *Trainspotting*. Perhaps there is always that minimum level of entry, on the part of secret things, into the field of the known. We know about MacPherson of Cluny only because he came down, we know of the dead Frenchman only because he was found. A disputed element of his story involves the possible presence of a second man, who travelled with him but left the scene alone. From the position in which he was found, the dead man had ensured he would slump backwards, gone but ideally placed to take in the whole panorama in that unknowable moment of final extremity.

§ 54

I am standing in the doorway trying to zip up my child's coat before we go out, and they are telling me a story about how it was Christmas Eve and 'Wibbly Pig was investigating'. My fingers are fumbling with the zip-piece and I'm pretty sure they don't know what 'investigating' means. The coat is green and I will sometimes call them Mr Green, a label that sticks in my mind even when they're wearing something else, like their less-favoured brown coat. I think of how often that noted Austrian philosophical investigator Ludwig Wittgenstein would use the banalest of details, from grinding your teeth to drumming your fingers, to make a point about language, and how we inhabit its protective covering without always knowing what it means, or even what what it means means. If I told you Mr Green – an actual Mr Green this time – was wearing a green coat, would you switch mentally from one kind of green to the other while you listened? Suppose you thought accidentally of green the colour while saying Mr Green's name – would that be wrong? We put on and stand inside our words like my child inside their coat, waiting to go on our wee journey or be taken on it by them. Mr Ireland is English. Ms English is from Ireland. Dr Scott is a Scot. (My child appears to believe, for whatever reason, that 'Scottish' means good: 'I'm very Scottish at playing the bagpipes', they will tell me.) Wittgenstein did not read novels but looked to go to cowboy movies, in which he took a childlike pleasure. Stories like this about the thinker abound, as though revealing a hidden higher wisdom. What could he possibly have meant by liking cowboy movies rather than reading *Ulysses*. Perhaps it meant he enjoyed cowboy movies. Am I being profounder than profound if I too like *Wibbly Pig*? One day we will grow into understanding, but while we wait the coat is still a coat, it still keeps the rain out. Can we go now? For the moment it is I who am holding us up until the zip connects at last. Wittgenstein visited Scotland once, on his way to Iceland, where, in his pre-ascetic phase, he lived it up in an expensive hotel. 'Ding dong,' says my child, though we are closing rather than opening the door. If I could stand here just a moment longer inside the shell of my words, I might unpick the knot of puzzles we carry with us across the park to the café. 'Ding dong,' they say when we get back, and look, it opens this time, the fresh crumbs of their pancakes smeared round their mouth as their mother comes to the door to scoop them up, Mr Green, our laughing child already spilling out of their big billowing coat.

§ 55

Tintin is sailing to the Dark Isle, head framed in little beads of anxious ectoplasm. The islands frame the mainland in their own halo of nervous afterthoughts. This island is four hundred miles from the last, but whichever we are on it is 'the island', only ever 'the island'. But there is an island within the island, tucked in and furtive, moored halfway up the long brown tongue of the inver, bobbing with shearwaters and guillemots. On the storm beach a lone rowing boat, and then up the shore the large white house. Tales would circulate of the long-dead lady of the house. The bullet, where she had shot herself in the head long decades since, proved impossible to remove. She was childish and incontinent, and given to rambling monologues. She had been treated not in a casualty ward but a maternity hospital. She was far from helpless, and would drive about the countryside picking up airmen to 'interrogate'. She would have herself rowed across for dances in the village. Herr Hitler had been simply the most wonderful dancer. Every day she took lunch at the same restaurant as the Fuehrer, hoping to attract his attention. Her middle name was Valkyrie, and her dramatic newspaper letter ('I want everyone to know I am a Jew hater') insisted on giving her name in full, her Jew-hate not being something she felt minded to conceal. It was the most frightfully exciting time all round. Of course her sisters took different views of these questions, but they were hardly going to allow something like that to come between them. The trick is to talk trivially of serious things and seriously of trivial things. In the harbour we see an otter board a trawler, sporting with the controls as though minded to take off for Oban. I have noticed on these islands there will often be a functional road on the eastern side and then a hair-raising track round the west where the sheep and their farmers live. The weather deteriorates and the waterspouts on the braeside over the strait begin flowing, blowing upwards into the air like geysers. I notice a hard sectarian edge to the banter round the screens when the football is on in the pub. Soon there is nothing left to see out the window all day but the haar, with somewhere the passing ferries inside it. I ask a man at the other end of the bar about the sectarianism and he tells me it is nothing personal, it's just the ritual things people say. Later we will return here and marry in brilliant sunshine, and one day we will revisit with our children and tell them what we remember of these times. Among the rumours about the property on the smaller island is that the lady of the house scratched a swastika into the glass of her bedroom window. When trying to be polite she would say, 'Although we are not on the same side, I am pleased to be among you.'

§ 56

Researcher: n/a

Research output title: n/a

Research environment commentary: The impetus for this research output (attached) came from a preliminary discussion with my line-manager in light of my recent work on [diagnosis for] [protected term] and their proposal that, in light of our existing strengths in the field, having first secured funding, and benchmarking the project outcomes against [what], I should then [something]. Among the research fingerprints associated with this project are [cut and paste], and though building on the work of [someone] I have chosen to avoid the label of [unnamed] altogether, for reasons I ['d rather not say]. To reach the stage of articulating a life-event that in its original context was experienced as [protected term] implies a degree of distance [manipulation] bringing with it complex questions of [artistic commodification], which I have chosen to [ignore]. I chose the title *Stretto* for reasons of [I liked it]. My research practice has involved [sitting at kitchen table/ rephrase]. Often the writing process has resembled nothing so much as a slot machine. You put something in and something might come out, or not. Since developing these research interests [/having long carried around these random obsessions], I have aspired to give them a more developed form. Or: I have played in the park with a toddler this morning and noted down what they said, for writing up later. Questions are raised of the social prestige enjoyed by different forms of research/things you write on your hand. Reading author interviews I note the frequency with which writers describe writing their books at 'the top of the house', which I take to be a signal that they inhabit three-storey homes. I have written this research output principally on envelopes I carry about on my person, bundled into trousers and jacket pockets. When the chance presents itself, I transcribe them onto a laptop computer, which I am sometimes compelled to borrow from my children. There is therefore that sense of moving between worlds in the composition process itself. Different occasions invite different stylistic registers, and even writing this database entry (which no one will read), there is an expectation that a degree of formalities will be observed. But a certain slippage can also be observed. In summary, if invited to characterise my research practice/my sitting idly at the kitchen table, I would point to this slippage. A research project [metaphysical quest] is glimpsed and pursued, the quest fails, and the idea is redefined in ways that allow the research ['metaphysical quest'] to go on; but in reality no progress has been made, and the plans and statements I draw up in my defence (such as this one) are the merest exercises in saving face. Writing of this kind is essentially defenceless, or indefensible. It is a form of exposure to psychological hazard and willingness to endure, the better to record, the sorry consequences. I understand the importance of keeping this database regularly updated, since external examiners will be working in the first instance from this description of the work rather than the work itself. I understand that these external examiners may end up writing their reports on the basis of this précis rather than the work itself.

[*Save draft?*]

§ 57

I have travelled very little in my life and always regretted it.
I have not found what I set out to, or perhaps was looking for
the wrong thing, or not looking for anything. On one occasion
I found myself on the other side of the world, and could not
believe my eyes. I noticed the earth was a different colour from
what I was used to and, having looked carefully, at all times
of the day, decided to check my impressions against the landscape paintings in the national gallery. But these only added to
my confusion by matching the landscapes I had left behind on
the other side of the world, the chestnut brown soil of Europe
rather than the bright red earth I was seeing all round me.
Acclimatising myself to this strange new landscape, I decided
that these nineteenth-century artists had picked up their train-
ing in Europe and arrived here unprepared to record this new
reality. For long decades, then, realist painting in the style I
am describing here operated at an oblique angle to reality, or
the reality I had witnessed at least. Perhaps it had been too
much to take in, or perhaps I too in my disorientation was getting it wrong – mistaking what they had seen, what I too was
seeing. Years later and long returned home I discovered the
books of a writer from that far-away country and noticed how
much he also was exercised by questions of orienting himself in
the landscape, and the sense he often gives off of experiencing
something like sea-sickness on dry land. While his travelling
to Europe might have caused him a share of disorientation, he
has never done so, staying close to home all his life. He is noto-
rious for it, even, in the melodramatic accounts of commenta-
tors compelled to pathologise a small harmless difference such
as this. Aware that he works as a barman in a golf clubhouse

in a small rural town (this too is part of his legend), I write him a letter. He is gracious enough to reply with a series of impressions on the themes I had developed. He has lived in a kind of trance, he tells me. His region is largely flat, but in the corner of his eye, as he looks out over it in one direction, there are some hills. These hills bear the same name as the hills in my region, or one of their names at least, as bestowed on them (his hills, I mean now) by settler colonials remaking the new world in their image. So small in the distance, they issue a daily challenge to the plainsman to forsake his easy flatlands and experience the rigours of verticality. But where do their demands begin and end, is he within or without the region of their command. I answer the call of the placename, slip between the old-world originals they shadow, here where I live, and their antipodean namesakes. As sunlight overtakes shadow, I instinctively shield my eyes, since the sun in my correspondent's homeland I remember as a mortal enemy. He adjusts the blinds in the golf clubhouse and my eyes on the other side of the world open on shadow again.

§ 58

And press record: 'Hello . . . you have to say words . . . good-bye'. Stop. Our child has discovered a dictaphone, otherwise a 'sound jumble', and carries it round to record their morning routine. In doing so they are overlaying an old recording of one of us hammering out a Beethoven sonata on the piano, creating a crazy tapestry of past and present. For reasons of narrative continuity (its hero is already an old man in the 1950s), *Krapp's Last Tape* is set in the future. One aspect of this not thought through by Beckett is technological obsolescence, the tendency of recordings made on once-new forms of technology to become unplayable. Though Krapp's recordings remain functional, his rejection of them on the human level accelerates the shift whereby the archive replaces the event. The past is there but why revisit it, compelled though we feel to do so. Our child's recordings draw on no Krappian depths of remembrance, circling instead round their performative moment ('Hello . . . hello . . . goodbye') with rapid bursts of arithmetic thrown in ('seven minus eight plus one is zero . . . a million plus a million is two . . .'). On my telephone calls home I notice how much of the dialogue circles round the same performative moment ('Hello . . . are you there . . . is there a delay on the line . . .'). Newer forms of technology such as the mobile phone or video-conferencing apps are worse for this, I find, not better. A dark suspicion that the conversations we have anyway, these problems aside, are glorified versions of the same questions. Are you there, can you hear me. But this too, this account of our child's play, forms part of a report, notes for a report. Previously photographs were occasions, but now they are running commentaries. You might have tens of thousands of the things on a phone, but to what end. I was there, says the photograph. 'As no art is, /Faithful and disappointing', runs the poem about photography by my erstwhile local poet. Not so, we overlay the image with a doctored version of our choosing, as we see fit. Also: the non-filtered version taken by your camera differs radically from the equivalent on mine, I notice, so what is the image really, even without filters, what is the true 'original' on which we ring our changes. I see a photograph of you and forget I was ever there: the photograph not just records but replaces the moment. Is it my job to go through this record and sift, analyse, understand. No. My daily recordings in these notes overwrite the 'stupid bastard' I took myself for twenty or thirty years ago, but who remains there, even when silent, the ostinato bass on which I perform inelegant variations. These notes are designed to be filed, not read, they are silent music. I speed up, I slow down. Hello. You have to say words. Goodbye. Abandon your sound jumble and flee to the woods: there are badgers there, Hamish the cat sits high in the yew tree, pass through its low-stooping branches and stand inside it yourself. As recorded here, as hereby recorded, date-stamped, filed and – down the hatch – gone.

§ 59

To live in a Barratt-home box as we have done in recent times has, I realise, shaped the course of these notes in significant ways. Where our previous house would crumble away and sink into the earth, in all the ways I have detailed, this one does not. Or so the theory runs. With the peculiar upshot that it may be in worse condition than our previous home, as I have given no thought to its maintenance at all, and looking at it now see multiple damp patches on the ceiling, small mushroom colonies growing in corners of the garage. To live surrounded as I do by couples of breeding age, and to be party to one such couple, as I am, this too will have unconsciously guided the drift of my thoughts. Here I am fitting in, a respectable member of the community at last, I can lend you a snow-shovel should you need one, or perhaps you'd prefer an allen key, I've got loads, in a drawer. But a counterexample. I am aware of an unoccupied house by the graveyard, wreathed in Virginia creeper: several of its windows are boarded up, and those that aren't include broken panes, with nothing visible behind them, where two such windows look out blindly onto the road. Two wheelie bins lie in a state of disrepair on their sides. It is autumn and the apple trees in the garden have become dramatically overladen, so we decide to enter and carry out a small but unlicensed harvest. After some minutes of doing this I noticed an upstairs light has come on. A naked bulb starkly framed and the only detail in an attic window. Perhaps it is on a sensor. Or perhaps there is someone there. A wild-haired old woman, forgotten by friends and family, turning over and over the events in the manse so many years ago now. How does she eat. What does she do with her waste. Should she hazard a glance above the parapet and risk being seen. Hands on the windowsill, long uncut nails brushing against the odds and ends of dead flies and moths, their tiny bedlam, a beldam's bedlam. From where she lies she sees Venus rise. She. Who she. I am drawn in by the blank façade more so than I would be by a neighbour's house, for reasons most likely bound up with the occupation I practise of my own domestic space, and my bad faith about this. I ponder the innumerable small furry hooks probing, loosening, slowly destroying the brickwork, and hear another over-ripe apple hit the ground outside. I celebrate the unknowability of our lives, even to ourselves, and scowl resentfully in the direction of the window, think about raining missiles down on their heads, the apple-thieves, whoever they are, but no, not this time, I turn the light off again and return to bed safe for another featureless day in the Virginia-creeper house.

§ 60

But then to find a railway carriage in the woods, bright red, on the high ridge of a rutted path. In the windows are further, miniature railway carriages, the one thing inside the other. When I was young and travelling into the city, I would often find myself sitting in the empty train in the station, waiting for it to move and looking through the window at up to two more trains on the station's other platforms. Then there would be movement and for a brief moment uncertainty too, as first I assumed it was my train moving, before I registered my immobility, and that it was that other train pulling out instead. I particularly remember the effect when there were two other trains, because of the different permutations this enabled. If the furthest train was the one to move, I would still have that other stationary train between me and it, and see it depart through a series of aligned windows. There was also, on the far platform wall, a series of murals illustrating trains of bygone times, ending with a representation of the train in which I was sitting, though logically it might have ended with a representation of me too, passenger in that train, visible to me from the train window. To judge from the livery, our railway carriage here in the woods appeared to be of early twentieth-century vintage. The line – multiple lines – had closed and farmers often bought up rolling stocks; I have even seen cows standing ruminating with their heads poking out of carriage windows whose glass has fallen out. While juddering back and forth between the woods and my hometown railway station, I notice my child has found a telephone box, also bright red, which advertises itself as a teleportation booth, with comic instructions about not travelling during summer months to avoid the risk of transporting midges to other planets. Having explained all this to them, I notice my child's method of initiating teleportation is to bend their knees and dance on the spot while making loud whooshing noises. As they travel from planet to planet, I notice they make a point of returning to earth between each one. Yet when I pick up the telephone receiver to make a call from space they become irate, informing me there are no telephones in space. I hardly needed this reminder of the terrible seriousness of a child's play, but I am struck by the importance to their journeys outwards of a constant to-and-fro, or there-and-back. But what about the railway carriage over there, I would ask, on 'Mars'. No Daddy, that's the earth train, we can't go in that, comes the reply, suggesting the carriage is both there and not there at once, but even when not remains available as a reference point. Are we moving yet, I ask of our teleporter. Yes, we're moving, no, we're there now. Open the door, close the door. If we're not moving, they must be moving, over there, mammy and sibling, if they're not moving it must be us.

§ 61

For a long time now I have woken up early. If you have been in a car crash you might have the experience of waking and experiencing the briefest moment of unremembering, of consciousness as blank slate for the day ahead before the weight of memory tumbles back down. I have not been in a car crash or anything like it, but am keen to isolate this moment of openness and possibility. Is it an aberration, a dangling appendix of time-consciousness left over from infancy and serving no adult purpose, or is it the truth of consciousness, otherwise hidden under the dead weight of waking habit. Out the window is a line of recently-built houses with, visible through an upstairs window, the unexpected shimmer of a disco ball. When the first spade went in the ground I cursed the builders for spoiling my view of the forest behind, as someone will have done when the spade went in the ground to build the house in which I now lie. One aspect of living here is the length and brevity of the hours of daylight, depending on which end of the year we are in. And then on top of that the strange sense, in the troughs of winter or summer, of their immutability: it will always be dark when you wake, when you go to work, and then by early afternoon again; there will always be sunlight over the hills at half-past ten at night, always this room will be a cube of light at four in the morning. Both can't be true yet both are, in that moment, that unmoving instant in which I dig in, inwards and downwards. Often I will be woken by the small person beside me, whose oneiric stream of consciousness comes tumbling out without any preliminaries or explanation. *And then the cows went up in a hot-air balloon but I chased them and you can't do **that** I said.* But on rare occasions it is I who wake first, and experience a state of rest more soothing than sleep by merely lying there under a weighted blanket, and as though burrowing downwards with my elbows. It cannot be more restful than sleep, but the waking consciousness of what I am doing seems to make that difference. As also does being under the weighted blanket: to lie above the sheet or sheetless is not an option, whatever the weather. How I regulate my temperature from winter to summer is a mystery, but suggests the cocoon comes first, as a felt bodily need, with my temperature lagging behind, a poor second. I shiver or bake and don't notice, thinking only of my cocoon and the slippage of consciousness from dreamstate to waking. It is winter or summer and I remain oblivious, thinking only of that moment when light and dark are the light and dark of the skull and my eyelids open, savouring for that instant the coincidence of what awaits me with that rush of passing through the portal, from world to world, to this of all worlds, in which a child stretches, wakes and kicks me, laughing hard, in the balls.

§ 62

Lose a degree celsius for every five-hundred feet climbed.
Nearly ten degrees on the big peaks off to the west, Braeriach,
Ben Macdui, Cairn Toul. Floating away there I feel my breath
bubble into a northern dazzle of ice, seen by no one. Blin drift,
sneepa, owerblaw, skifter, feucher, skirlie, wauff, all framed in
the car window. We pull in on our travels by a forest entrance,
and leaving the wipers off are soon encased. I have to blow it
away with my dragon's breath, Daddy. Or how about we leave
the wipers off, drive blind deeper and deeper into the white.
Better to keep on the move than have the wind's teeth sink in
our heels. Our words tunnel ahead of us, worming into the
small ears of the mountain fox, each new word walking in the
prints of the last. In a way Nansen never set foot on the Arctic,
crossing instead this snowy pseudo-surface we tread now. Like
the radioactive cloud sea in *Solaris*, the snow is there yet not. I'm
putting this part of the mountain in my pocket, Daddy, we'll
climb it again later on. I see you, Malcolm Mooney, pacing
beside us as we go, off at the edge of earshot. You want to be up
at the pools where the Don and Dee rise, practising for future
whisky as they fall. What is the attraction of this drifting element, this landscape both epic and evanescent. When I studied
the valley near Invercauld with the map-maker, he got down
flat on his chest. He had written the placenames on labels,
attaching them to low-hanging leaves. On the large kitchen
table he spread out sheaves of maps, one on top of another.
The languages too are arranged one on top of another. Some
Gaelic names for hills include beinn, càrn, creag, tòrr, cleit,
sgùrr, stob, stùc, stac, bidean, meall, maol, ceann, mullach,

druim, aonach, gualann, sròn, sìdhean, àrd, bràigh, monadh, mòine, cnoc, bàrr, cnap, òrd, tulach, tom, dùn, màm, cìoch, suidhe, cathair, caisteal, buachaille, cailleach. I thought serac was a dependably Nordic word for ice, but it turns out to be a French word for cheese. Every year the snowpatch watchers get terribly excited about the patches that manage to linger, from one winter to the next. I feel I ought to learn Old Norse or Norn, it seems somehow rude not to, in discussing these things. But there is an element of unquestioned racial white-ness in some people's cult of the north, unquestionably. When Franklin set off to discover the north-west passage and was lost, a second expedition found his ship, and was treated by Inuits to tales of cannibalism among the ice-bound sailors. Among those outraged at this was Dickens, who could not not believe white men would sink to such a depravity. We are meant to cover these surfaces as though not physically there, suitors of a disembodied ice queen. But the snow will melt into foul spring slush, and a false step on the mountainside drop me up to my middle in a quag. Not much purity there. Figures move through a landscape. They will not find what they seek. Daddy, are we there yet, there's nothing here, go back go back.

§ 63

Sounds travel but silence travels, silence echoes too. Explain. It is a small blue and black cassette, it is Joni Mitchell's *Blue*. To be played on a battery-operated cassette player, ten songs, with the smallest of adjustments needed to get us over the step from side one to two, from 'Blue' to 'California'. To be played in my room, wherever that is, this or that room, here or there. Once again, there is in the retrieval of memory always this technological aspect. While the sound quality of an ancient cassette differs markedly from that of a contemporary stream-ing service, the tracks' envelope of silence also differs, then from now. 'I want to make you feel free, /I want to make you feel free': ends. Then count. One two three four: 'The wind is in from Africa'. Another silence I would recognise anywhere, that leads only from that first song to the second. Rather than turn straight over and stitch two songs together: no. Or hit the hyperspace fast-forward or rewind buttons, landing who knows where in the sound jumble: also no. But how many listeners now know what side one and side two are anymore, or grasp the audacious placing of the heartbroken 'Blue' at the halfway point rather than the end, and then that sudden reanimation with 'My Old Man' when we change sides. That cultural moment seems very specific and unrepeatable, just as Mitchell's songs did at the time for anyone who tried to play them, with their multiple unique tunings, and the challenges they represented in live performance (solved through an ingen-ious system of remote tuning by a technician offstage). When I select this or that track now, not on cassette, and no longer the full album, the silences have gone. In the sense that I can skip around however I want, but also in the deeper sense that the silences between tracks are no longer the same. In Beckett's *Krapp's Last Tape* (again), there is a sharp contrast between the man onstage and the recordings he plays of his younger self, a self he struggles to recognise, resulting in multiple rewindings and fast-forwards. The voice on the tape comments harshly on the younger Krapp again, whose recordings *he* has been listening to. The technology has preserved the past while also laying bare the poverty of the commodified, mechanical form it assumes, from which Krapp recoils in horror. But what does he want, really, what is he looking for. At the end of the play he sits in silence pondering his many failures. As he does so he allows the now-silent tape to carry on playing. But of course it isn't silent, since the unwieldy machine squeaks and rattles to itself as the tape-heads go round. Here at last is an element (silence) in which then-Krapp and now-Krapp can be united, even if only in a shared sense of failure. Today Joni Mitchell is unwell and has not recorded for years. I do still have a cassette recorder, however, and have found my tape of *Blue* in the garage. 'Here is a shell for you, /inside you'll hear a sigh.' This is not nostalgia. There is nothing to be nostalgic about. I hear that sigh. Now turn over.

§ 64

One country may conceal another. And then behind that, and that. I have taken a hammer to the archipelago and smashed it into innumerable small floating bits. One map may lurk behind another, the maritime northern fringes full of shark's teeth ready to devour all previous efforts. Russian submarines plant flags underwater to claim as-yet unborn land. A British explorer attempts to claim a new volcanic island in Norway. If the sea fell and the land bridge between this island and that returned, to whom would it belong. And here on an empty shore among the northern isles I find a new nation, the Sovereign State of Forvik. Events in the fifteenth century have left its constitutional status unclear, argues its founder. No one lives here, there is nowhere to live. I gather camping is not unknown. It shows more signs of life on the internet, where its founder, a much-shipwrecked sailor, peddles his theories of 'allodial title' to land ownership, meaning land in these parts is not subject to any superior landlord (i.e. the sovereign). These theories he expounds in much the same spirit as a hairdresser in the news who claim that Magna Carta means they are not obliged to comply with pandemic lockdown restrictions. In the 1930s Hugh MacDiarmid lived in a place called Sodom on nearby Whalsay and pondered the autonomous self among the stones: 'I ken these islands each inhabited / Forever by a single man / Livin' in his separate world as only / In dreams yet maist folk can.' He confronted the absolute non-human, or did he, was that really what was on his mind. Some have suggested his crisis was caused by falling down the stairs on a London tram and landing on his head. A syphilitic infection had by now also rendered him impotent (and, no small consideration, unable to scan). He describes being dropped on a smaller island alongside Whalsay, West Linga, and having his mystical experience there, but this is disputed. Perhaps it never happened. During the war a secret policeman moves to the island and follows the poet around, as he cadges food off local fishermen and lies in the heather. In 'Harry Semen' he writes about the ultimate miniature monad of his sperm, circulating like dogfish or massing together like snowstorms. His vision culminates in the Virgin Mary's immaculate conception. But his own seed falls on stony soil. Does it at least impregnate the rock. To what will the rock give birth. I have coupled with the inhuman and desire progeny from it. Or was it it that coupled with me. I feel my circulation slow down, and what is that lurking under the patch of dry skin on my arm. Stone in my veins. In the gaps in the dry-stone broch petrels are nesting invisibly. At dusk they make unearthly music, which I mistake for the cry of the broch itself. And then the ragged island graveyard is the broch where the dead go nest, their headstones the slowest of slow-hatching limbs, sprouting up out of the earth.

§ 65

Child, your name means 'great mountain'. I take you to the
top of the village to spy your namesake mountain in the distance. Then I am told this is not the peak I thought it was, but
one further off to the south. Is it – are you – visible after all,
I wonder. Maybe that one over there. There is another one of
you, I am aware, far off in the frozen north. Sprung from the
landscape, run to the woods now, your hands full of flowers;
and can I come with you, I hear them sing, the harebells and
cranesbill, the women's tongues singing under the grass. Little
I knew, Nighean Dhonncha cries out to you, rising early in
Glenlyon on Lammas morning, that soon my heart would be
crushed. It's far rather I'd be with Gregor, roaming moor and
copse than with the skinflint Baron of Dull in a house of lime
and stone. *Hé mandu, hi ri o ró, hó ro hù ó*, where can I see a man
of his likeness now Fionn and Oscar are not living. Alasdair
sailed his birlinn through the Sound of Luing, sang Diorbhail
to you, and in that moment I gave him my heart. How I loved
that company, the folk of the brown and the yellow ringlets
who made the yew bow buckle and drank of the red wine in
billows, *e-hó hi u hó, ró hó eile*. When a Campbell trampled my
grave and cursed me, Duncan Maclachan sent for a gallon of
whisky, and had it drunk on the spot to my memory. Màiri
Nighean Alasdair Ruaidh walked about with a silver-tipped
staff and affected whisky and snuff. What left me tearful, she
sang to you, was to see the land blighted, now Iain Garbh's
chimney no longer reeked, under the wave-lashed rock. Thinking my praises too much, Roderic Mòr sent me away. When he
allowed me back, it was under pain of my no longer composing

within my house or without. I sat on the threshold murmuring to myself, between two worlds, and was buried face down as a witch. Girl from the village, girl from above, it is you whose form casts a haze on the stars. *Hi hó hi ri o ró*, travelling early I saw your vessel come over the sea from Canna, the ship of my baby, the ship of the islands, *Hi hó hi ri o ró*. The whale blows in the monstrous tides but where is the fear: no harm can befall you, sang all these voices to you, from under the grass. Baby, my baby, where are you going but off to the woods, you are the outlaw and you are the bard, you are the cloud and you are the mountain. I would follow you to the loch in the wood, I would follow you where the wolf keeps his lair. All this you know, all this and more, leap like the salmon about your play, you carry the flowers of the earth in your hands and carry the sun in your hair, *Hi hó hi ri o ró.*

§ 66

A vintage children's programme we watch together shows its bowler-hatted hero embarking on a series of fantastical journeys. Entering a costume shop he is pointed upstairs to a changing room by a fez-wearing shopkeeper, after which he passes through a second door for his adventures. Nevertheless, a certain schematism is apparent. He will typically encounter a man in a position of authority who takes charge, such as the fellow astronaut who suggests they visit a nearby planet to extract its mineral wealth. The colonial dimension receives a rather bland treatment, as does the apparent absence from our hero's universe of people unlike him. Why go to outer space to encounter a simulacrum of yourself when you can lean over the garden fence of your spacious suburban property. Do we need a stop-go animated version of *Solaris*, I ask myself, a three-hour exploration of guilty exile and return with a hero plagued by visions of his long-suffering wife, whose requests that he walk the dog before going to work he has for many years resisted. Oh Trevor, I don't ask much. But with you gone all day, then polishing the Wolseley in the drive after dinner most evenings . . . Come on, says our hero's new friend, let's try this planet instead. And on they go before boredom sets in and the shopkeeper reappears to lead them home. I have come to see this waistcoated figure as the keeper of a Victorian opium den, with his elaborate courtesies and pandering to the gentleman's needs. As his customer, our hero takes his place in a long line of escapist protagonists for whom work means stability without challenge, gently persecuted by his remorseless accumulation of wealth without any need to grow as a human. I didn't get where I am today by growing as a human, I imagine CJ telling the hero in *The Rise and Fall of Reginald Perrin*, while the squeaking sound of a rear end meeting a leather office chair triggers a cut-away vision of a waddling hippopotamus, a long-running stand-in for his feared and loathed mother-in-law. Back at home in the cartoon, everything is as our hero left it. Boys play with toy rockets while their mothers bring home the shopping. Boys play with lifting the corner of the narrative fabric and seeing what lurks behind it. Get under the covers Daddy, we're going to 'Back', announces our child, a planet where the parental back is pinched energetically (and quite painfully), over and over. Open the rocket door. We've come to Back. We pinch the Back. Don't move Daddy, this is Back. I realise that I am both planet and fellow explorer. But suppose we pinch *your* back. No! And isn't it time to go back to earth now. No, we live here now, on 'Back'. But what do we do all day. We pinch, Daddy. Can we ever go back? Go . . . 'back'! We could go back to Back later? 'Back!' This goes on for quite some time. The child clearly differentiates 'Back' from 'go back', but finds their pretend-refusal to do so endlessly funny. Someone help please. The barrier between here and there has gone missing, and the waistcoated shopkeeper is wandering lost through the aisles of costumes unable to find and lead us . . . 'Back!'

§ 67

I dress in the dark and mistake a small shirt-collar button for a regular button and comically misbutton my shirt. I put my jumper on both backwards, or is it inside out, which, I will find out later. I tie my shoes only for them to fall open again, at which point I do not attempt to make good my mistake. All day people will point this out to me; there appears to be no polite way of disabling this response. Then drive to work and notice I have omitted to bring my keys. For long years I have traded, to myself as much as to others, on an idea of myself as too distracted to notice or get these things right, my mind on higher things. What a shambolic spectacle I must make, on a daily basis. Best not come to people's attention, then, I tell myself, walking the long way round to avoid random conversations, staying in my office when I hear voices. As chance would have it, I have been rereading the Mr Men, and notice how endemic this behaviour is among that star-crossed race. Poor Mr Wrong, putting his shoes on the wrong feet, tripping over the bathmat, putting the toothpaste on the wrong side of his toothbrush, and tripping down the stairs. Poor Mr Forgetful, tasked with informing a farmer that there is a sheep loose in the lane and announcing 'There's a goose in the rain'. Help is at hand, however. A strangely Mr Wrong-resembling Mr Right comes to stay with him and guide him back to functionality. In a comic twist, as Mr Wrong rights himself Mr Right begins to go wrong himself. Perhaps there is only so much functionality to go round. Also, I note in passing the peculiar fact of all the Mr Men living in detached houses in the countryside, their daily struggles, luckily for them, not having prejudiced their ability to find high-quality housing. A portrait of the ever-smiling Mr Happy, their apparent spiritual leader, beams down from a wall. The gender politics of Misterland, as I believe it is called, and its race of female stragglers – Little Miss Bossy, Little Miss Naughty – who turn up a decade after the Mr Men, I pass over in frigid silence. Is this funny, I ask my children. Yes, they tell me. Dyspraxia or developmental motor coordination disorder is a condition beginning in childhood and persisting into adulthood. When cooking once I became belatedly aware that the stove was not on, and I had been stirring, for quite some time, cold food. Pouring milk on his cornflakes Mr Wrong misses and gets it all over the table instead. Did you have difficulty finding this room, asks the nurse. How long has all this been going on. How have you managed all this time then, have you been as we say masking. Are you doing so now. Can you catch and return this ball. In ball games there is winning and losing. But what if, instead of returning the ball, I pick it up and put it in my pocket. What if this is not just a test but a test within a test, and only then do I win. Well, if it helps you to tell yourself that. Can you actually catch the ball though. No. 'That one again, Daddy, *Mr Wrong* again.'

§ 68

Crocodile, cro-co-dile. The child's violin technique is slightly unusual, squatting as they do over the instrument and drawing the bow across the strings with both hands, sometimes interrupting the playing to perform tiny leaps of celebration on their hunkers, pleased with how well it's all going. Their understanding of the chin-rest is also unusual. After a good old session sawing away, they announce both they and the instrument are tired. Down they lie with their chin on the rest. Another aspect of their relationship with the violin is a keen sense of its inside, of wanting to hear the notes echoing as they sound. It is their mother's violin, and though she no longer plays, I hear her play through our child. In her youth she played with Simon Rattle, our child's hero. Sometimes I fancy they believe they *are* Simon Rattle, conducting and playing all at once. In Wisconsin in the 1940s Lorine Niedecker began writing poems for Paul Zukofsky, the violin-playing son of her friend and former lover Louis Zukofsky. Niedecker lived in some poverty and isolation, and constructed a complex fantasy edifice around the young boy and his music, in ways that caused Zukofsky senior some discomfort. 'Now I must rake leaves', she wrote, 'with nothing blowing // between your house / and mine', casting herself as a figure in a distant landscape, far from the excitements of Chicago. Our child returns to his bowing and I think of the distinctive style of Donegal fiddling, lacking any vibrato and scratchy as a roll in a nettle-bed. Often the player will imitate a drone-effect on the G string, in ways that show the influence of the bagpipe tradition. Why the Donegal tradition should be so ascetic I don't know, as opposed to the more mellifluous

Sligo fiddling just down the road. Should they become a violin player in later life, will our child combine the classical and traditional styles, I wonder, code-switching maybe as Robert Burns does between English and Scots, one moment adding vibrato to their Vivaldi, the next scratching up clouds of resin with a rendition of 'The Glen Road to Carrick'. But what of the cello and the double bass, and the various other instruments round the house the child also plays. Which is to say, invisible instruments, including a church organ that requires climbing inside and vigorous footwork on the pedals. Dah dah DAH dah dah dah dah DAH DA. In later life Paul Zukofsky devoted himself largely to the modernist repertoire and cultivated a needlessly confrontational approach to scholars of his father's work, it seemed impossible to know what was going on inside his head. What he made of Niedecker's poems about him I can only imagine. Most famous of the Donegal fiddlers was John Doherty, a shaman-like figure whose recordings combine languor and ferocity in ways that defy easy description. Is it true, I wonder, that travelling tinsmiths, such as his family, made brass fiddles. Could a brass fiddle be played, and what would it sound like. Doherty himself did not own a fiddle. And why should he, he must have thought, there is always one in the house wherever I go.

§ 69

Travelling with a toddler to the planet Saturn in a large space-ship-shaped mausoleum in a country churchyard, one naturally takes a moment to study the graves. It's a gas giant, Daddy, you can't walk on it. We climb in behind the rusty grill and the journey begins. Dead at twenty-five, beloved wife of. Close the hatch. Also the former, four decades later. Ten nine eight. Also a second wife of the above, another twenty-five years later, and also again the infant child of the first marriage, in the one grave. The rings of Saturn are made of ice. What would the position be on polygamy in the hereafter. It has eighty-two moons. A sprinkling of *died tragicallys* is only to be expected, the teenager in a car smash followed the next year by a parent, dissolved in grief and the clinking bottles purchased wordlessly at the Co-op. I'm just going over here now, look, there's a shed. In one corner an inscription for an unmarked grave that lies outside the wall, in the suicide's copse: a memorial to a non-memorial. To think a limit is to go beyond it, that thin meniscus between living and dead. The soil rolls over the farmer's grave and the son or next brother along will take the tractor over the hill where the peewits flutter madly over the upturned clods as the snell spring breeze returns. The land will have you and hold you, this generation or that, strong is its grip. But to wake at dawn to no harrow awaiting my unwashed palm, no hay to save, to neeps to sned, where have I misplaced my patrimony. My corpses lie scattered over a hillside over the water, my parents and siblings gather for their small celebrations without me. But we have to collect samples, Daddy. To be fifty years of age, no longer young, my knees know it better than I, when I stoop to put the child on my shoulders, when I stoop to disturb the earth on the site of my grave. As time passes, the map of childhood places I might recognise has lost all urban space with its redrawn roads and carnival of self-reinvention. The mountain tops, the bogs up over the bay I remember, enduring in intrinsic flux, there's no changing that. Three two one blast-off, standing inside the mausoleum now and peering through the grill at the tottering crosses. To be no longer young, the essence of mature male ebbed away like a dribble of juice shaken from the food caddy after the binmen have been, the dregs emptied into the soil bed. A shade melodramatic perhaps, but still. Here we affect a measured tone – 'Dearly loved father, loved mother . . .' – thinking the better of these modest displays even as we stage them, give us a peeling limestone grave and let it moss over and fall away into the grave of a grave, the bits of slabs the sexton drags off to that metal shed. We have what we need Daddy, we can go back to our planet.

§ 70

Buster Keaton is dangling from a level-crossing pole as a driverless car approaches from the distance. The pole falls, he lands in the driver's seat, and off he goes, even if the car falls apart shortly afterwards. How did he do it. In a documentary clip, he talks about never working from scripts, though I presume he at least dabbed a chalk mark on the road to suggest where the car should be before he began his descent. As we watch, my child begins to climb over me, jumping from a sofa arm onto the imaginary car of my lap and driving off. Something they and Keaton share is a wholly straight-faced commitment to the project, once begun. Keaton builds a boat and launches it, standing impassive on deck as it sinks and making no attempt to save himself. My child inverts themself and begins to climb inside my jumper, feet first. Keaton jumps from a roof and misses the adjoining building, then makes the best of slithering down the other side, before entering a handy window. But what are they on the run from? *Esse est percipi*, to be is to be perceived, as Beckett quotes in the epigraph to his *Film*, for which he secured the services of the elderly Keaton in 1965. On set, Keaton was unsure of what he'd got involved in, and kept suggesting visual gigs, such as paring a pencil down to nothing. His character is 'in flight from extraneous perception breaking down in the inescapability of self-perception'. Keaton is the man on the run from our gaze, even as he drags it with him. But gags will often take the form of escapes through unlikely openings and hatches, whose signals only Keaton sees, and whose winking gaze he slyly returns, as for instance when once again on the run he leaps and disappears into the case of her wares that a matchwoman wears around her neck. My child and I watch *The Railroader*, also from 1965, in which he crosses Canada in a miniature service engine, or 'speeder'. In one scene the speeder enters a tunnel and we see a point of light in the distance. It is the light at the end of the tunnel, I assume, until it approaches more closely and we see it is the speeder itself. The 180-degree inversion of perspective resembles the scene at the end of *Film* where Keaton has entered a room, sealed off all entrance points for prying eyes, only for his pursuer (implicitly the camera) to wheel round before him and meet his gaze directly. It is his own eye, staring into itself. He has escaped into an anti-portal, allowing no ingress or egress, only to pass through the portal of himself, even as he buries his eyes in his hands in despair. Confronting its impossibility the body is driven to comically desperate measures. Among Keaton's signature jokes in person was to place one foot on a table, and then the other too, succeeding in holding the pose for an instant before falling over. 'Will we walk around together with your feet in my jumper,' I ask my child, trying awkwardly to extricate myself. 'No, Daddy, we won't do that,' they snap. 'I'm just joking.' 'Don't joke.' 'I would never joke' (this exchange moves fast). 'You can't joke, you're not funny,' they retort, holding a straight face for a moment before erupting in laughter and disappearing into the sofa.

§ 71

What's that then, I ask the consultant. A diagnosis. What do I do with that. [*Pause.*] But is it not strange, I think, eyes drifting to the central green space overlooked by these windows on all sides, but without anything much to show for itself, a modest bench and a half-hearted water feature, is it not strange how the conditions you are describing remind me so strongly of figures of speech that I might explain to students in my line of work. Epistrophe, the repetition of the same word at the end of successive phrases. I think of the colour purple, my trains of thought all lead to that end-point, whether they start from a mountain, a seventeenth-century portrait, or Wallace Stevens' poem 'Tea at the Palaz of Hoon', that is epistrophe. Anadiplosis occurs if the associations are sequential, with one beginning where another leaves off, as in a sonnet corona, with final lines becoming first lines throughout: mountains become remote church becomes stained-glass window becomes the colour purple, but all to the same end. Metalepsis is a breaching of the boundaries between narrative levels, allowing us to move between worlds. This movement might be inwards or outwards, creating a sense of . . . passing through the stained-glass window in a mountain church and . . . as the examples build up, what others might see as neurology reveals itself on a deeper level as a question of style. You have to follow the vectors, follow where the words dry and riderless lead. I also see now what you mean by the 'special interests' and their tendency to loom large, freezing out everything else. Here is the jumper I have put on backwards, here is the shopping list I left at home, lacking all importance. And here is the Bach fugue I am playing silently on the table-top, here is the gleaming eye of a cat on a fence I have had to stop and study: you have to follow where the fugue subject leads, leap into the well of the cat's eye, there is in that moment nothing else. The train is not free to leave the tracks and randomly cross the terrain. Is this determinism then. No, it is freely chosen. There is no terrain, only the track. And is there movement, really, have I not always been there, been here. De Selby would travel by entering a wardrobe and thinking of his destination, then emerge to a sense of uncomprehending rage on not finding himself there. But it works, I have done it. I cross the mountain landscape and notice a church and, entering, find a stained-glass window and passing through it find myself in a mountain landscape where I notice a church and, entering, find a stained-glass window, god not this again, I am moving from one side of the glass to the other, turning madly on the spot, what figure of speech am I looking for now. These are not symptoms, these are figures of speech. So what are you suggesting I do, doctor. I call you doctor, but you are also the addressee, the reader, moving forwards and back through the text at your leisure. In this sense you are, have become, as much me as I am. Thank you for reading. How do you feel it's going? Now turn the page.

§ 72

I am walking in the snow and thinking of the word 'frazil', meaning ice crystals carried along a stream of water; I am thinking of the contrast between how free-floating the snow is as it falls and how obstinate and intractable it is once it hardens on the ground, hardens into ice patches on the pavement, at the side the house where I fooster with the bins late at night watched by a thousand granite eyes winking out from under their cover of frost. Why did Robert Frost write so well of frost, I wonder, could he have done so had his name been Robert Sunshine, no. 'The haar soukit in steam frae ever-bounteous stremis / is blawn heich abuin the yird by blaisters of wund', as Hesiod said, in Scots, who never looked at a puff of mist without seeing it radiate outwards from his Greek into possible mists and words for mists, and occupying that space, mist in a net, there and not there, held and free. I am focusing on the snow and ice, sculpting them into a fugue subject in the silent concert never not playing for me, mentally, when I realise the theme is already playing, remembered snow of ice from forty years previously, and the one is piling up on top of the other, stretto once more, that term again. Many people my age will remember a television ad from their youth for a breakfast cereal, consumers of which would walk around lit from within and emitting a kind of orange ectoplasm. I touch the snow and frost by the bin with the glow from within of decades past and feel the crystals on the bin-lid come off in my hand and turn to running water. If you cannot see your tracks behind you, Nan Shepherd said of her mountains, it is time to turn back. When the snow came, it was no longer possible for the fox to conceal her midnight trips to the garden. Will the snow still be there tomorrow, our child asked, but when there is more snow, not the same snow, they interpret this as a yes, that 'the snow' is still there. But how much snow is there, how is it measured. The correct answer to the question, to how many snow-flakes are falling, is simply 'many'. I calculate that temperature decreases by a degree Celsius with every five hundred feet or so gained. In the high mountains it forms into arches and caverns that will often survive the summer and reconnect with themselves the following winter. I have seen them myself. But are they there now, I wonder, as I invoke them here. I climb inside one on the side of Braeriach, with only the guts of the husky dog to warm me, when I slaughter the beast in my desperation, starving and astray in my wits, plunging my hands inside his pelt. The tunnel gives shelter, and acquires its own second skin, third, fourth skin, the joins are seamless, and glow upon glow I husband the obstinate fires of childhood, the flames turned inward, not out, frozen and preserved in all that whiteness.

§ 73

And did you know Father Coyle well? He always said a lovely mass. In fact I never knew him. I have attended his funeral by mistake. Wandering with a child I find the Catholic church in the woods, usually closed-up, open for an airing, or so I presume. In I wander and find all the familiar accoutrements: the large cross by the altar and its olive-toned Christ, some unremarkable stained-glass panels, and a waxen attar wafting from a store room, into which I wander. Though pleased to encounter stained glass in any form, this particular example does not immediately spark to life for me, or not in the way the stained glass recalled from my youth does – or could that be just the particular slant of light on the day that's in it, I wonder. But my meditations are suddenly interrupted by a commotion behind me as a congregation invisibly forms. It is Father Coyle's funeral. The child is now asleep in my arms. Standing in the door I can see a priest put on his flowing white vestments and stretching his arms, as though fitting a duvet into its cover. Of Father Coyle himself I learn little enough during the mass. It was a life of service. Eventually I break cover and mingle with the strangely unsurprised mourners, as though hibernating in a country church in the hope of awaking to a priest's funeral were the most natural thing in the world. With the departure of the funeral party the baby and I admire the work of the gravediggers, smoothing over the mound of earth on Father Coyle's plot behind the line of nuns' graves: Sister Mary Uriel, Sister Mary of Calvary, Sister Mary Pacificus . . . Later I will look them up and learn their convent in the nearby city had been the site of disturbing abuse. Incidents included children being locked in a cupboard for hours and being forced to eat their own vomit. Among the victim testimonies the court heard was that of a woman who no longer leaves the house, but spends her time obsessively cleaning. A phenomenon peculiar to true believers, I have found, is to respond to stories of this kind with 'But the nuns do great work.' I stand in the aisle again, between the worlds of the child-abusing nun and the light of grace filtered through the glass behind the altar. Is it an aesthetic pleasure I take then, I ask myself, I who lack faith. It all makes sense to the believer, but I just find it pleasant to look at. One can even experience art as a kind of semblance of belief. The better the art the closer the approach to the real thing, which I nevertheless reject, is that how it works. On belief and unbelief alike the sunlight through glass falls and I too am caught and transformed.

§ 74

I have come to the sea again, and am sitting in a high building looking out the only window at the blank line of the horizon, with on the wall a framed photo of a North Sea oil rig. A
midge is buzzing round the edge of the window, and on closer
inspection reveals itself as a helicopter come to carry me out
to the North Sea. I am carrying a slight cold, which has made
me experience the sound of my breathing like an insistent dog
standing by my ear, add to which the sound of the helicopter
blades on my flight, churning to atoms my sense of what is
solid and what not, of where air, sea and land begin and end.
The picture of the oil rig on the wall of the broadly identical
room to which I have travelled is the very oil rig on which I
have landed. Some oil fields are named for seabirds, others for
saints. I am sitting hundreds of feet above the north sea in a
locked cell looking out over the waves. What St Rona or Sula
Sgeir anchorite could have dreamt of this. My job involves the
opening up of holes in the earth's surface and the management
of what comes out. It could not be cruder or, simultaneously,
more precise. Shifts are twelve hours on and twelve hours off.
For those wishing to decompress after a shift, the smoking area
is entered and exited via a double-door system; nothing can go
wrong. On Piper Alpha, the safety cover for condensate pump
A was removed for maintenance, and a note left in the control
room that the pump was not to be used. This was then negli-
gently misplaced. When pump B suffered a routine blockage,
there was the shortest of windows for maintaining the flow
of oil, and the decision was made to restart pump A. In the
absence of a safety valve gas began to leak at high pressure,

triggering an explosion. 167 workers died. Of the 61 who survived, some, less badly injured, returned to work on the next shift, on a rig from which were visible the remains of Piper Alpha. A buoy now marks the spot. Today North Atlantic locations like Orkney or Shetland can seem marginal, shunted into a box in the corner of a map, but a millennium ago these places were strategically central, with Iceland, Norway, Denmark, the North of England and Scotland constellated round them. And so it is with a map of North Sea oil fields today. A worldview shared by saint, seabirds and rig workers. I look out the window and think how some Piper Alpha workers survived by jumping when told not to. Others jumped and died. None stayed and lived. I pass back through the window to the pebbled shore at dusk, looking for distant lights in the sea, batting away imaginary midges as another helicopter passes overhead.

§ 75

The style of fledging employed by gannets hatched in the great
coastal colonies of the North Atlantic admits little room for
error. After thirteen or so weeks the chicks throw themselves
off their cliff, hoping to land in the sea rather than bounce
to their death off the rocks. Once in the water they start to
swim, fishing as they go and building up their wing strength,
since for the moment they remain powerless to fly. One place
they might wash up as they swim is North Rona, one of the
furthest-scattered of the outlying North Atlantic islands. It has
not been continuously inhabited since the nineteenth century,
though subject before that to sudden depopulations during
smallpox epidemics and other natural disasters. In the seventh
century it attracted the Irish hermit Saint Ronan, the remains
of whose chapel can still be seen, and his sister Saint Brianuilt/
Brenhilda. The chapel measures 11 feet 6 inches by 8 feet, as
per the description of it to be found in F. Fraser's Darling's *A
Naturalist on Rona*. Finding the chapel in a rather overgrown
state, and littered with the debris of petrels' nests, he decides
to dig down and clear the floor. As he digs he encounters a
small chip of green Iona marble. That other consecrated island
lies 200 miles to the south; perhaps other pilgrims down the
ages have followed Ronan's path from the one to the other, or
perhaps the stone had lain there since the saint's own times.
Fraser's studies were interrupted by World War II, which
prompted his removal from the island by the Ministry of
Defence. In the previous world war, a German U-boat com-
mander was in the habit of stopping on the island to shoot sheep
for mutton. Does this constitute a German invasion, I wonder.

The opening of Ronan's cell, Darling establishes, would have been 4 feet 4 inches by 1 foot 8 inches. The insular Celts were strongly attracted to narrow entrances. But how would Ronan have lived, what would he have eaten. Did he fashion candles from the oil of cormorants? According to legend, St Brianuilt/ Brenhilda worshipped alongside her brother before his praising of her legs, in a moment of fleshy weakness, caused his sibling saint to flee to the rocky blip of Sula Sgeir twelve miles further west. Here too there are archaeological remains of a ruined chapel. How would the saint have got here though: did she fashion her own craft, did she travel with fishermen, did she swim or transform into a sea bird. A baby gannet, inches above the waves, is as dwarfed by a fisherman's currach as by the towering contours of Sula Sgeir appearing from nowhere. I am in the water and have swum all the way from the mainland. I feel my life flash before my eyes, but at the speed of life itself, slowly. To the point where the valedictory vision becomes indistinguishable from the thing itself, as encountered in what I am pleased to call everyday life. The one circles within the other, like the inner lining of a bicycle wheel, indispensable but invisible. But where to next, wheels within wheels. Beyond here is nothing.

§ 76

A child runs by in the castle garden, between two high hedges,
a barefoot Regency waif. The garden has been divided into four
quarters, each apportioned a century: seventeenth, eighteenth,
nineteenth and twentieth, and planted accordingly. I hear the
child's voice and run in pursuit, but the maze of hedges is complex, and turning the corner I find a blank wall with the sound
of laughter echoing behind me now. Doubling back to another
corner I bump into the child, dislodging the Victorian stove-
pipe hat they are now wearing. We are distracted from this
mishap by the sound of a dove apparently nesting in the hedge
beside us, and stand for a moment admiring its rhythmic roo-
coo-cooing. I have wandered down endless corridors in search
of you, I announce. No response. We met here last year, I add.
Still nothing. You made me promise to come back, now, today.
But the child has run off again, in the direction of the Shake-
spearean roses. Try to remember, I say, as much for my benefit
as that of the now-vanished child. Watch carefully. An object,
a gesture, a view. This rendering in spatial form, before my
eyes, of temporal zones is well established now, let us not affect
to find anything out of the ordinary in all this. Here is the zone
of the homeland: all I have to do is adjust my glasses – so – and
the long road we are walking down together will come out at
my childhood home. Here is the zone of the second country,
behind these doors, with everyone I will meet there waiting to
raise their eyes and meet mine when they swing shut behind
me. Here we are now is the third zone, that of the present,
perhaps the most difficult to get into focus. And here behind
my back is the zone of the unknown, down this hedge-lined

avenue still echoing to the laughter of a vanishing toddler. You promised me we would sit in the pergola. I had counted on it, to persuade myself that the memories I have carried from last year have not been an illusion. I talk of past, present and future, and move promiscuously between them, with only you as my anchor in all this flux. I might escape into the future but have chosen to double back here, but do I bring the – am I the chaos I have tried to escape. Daddy, you dropped your hat, says the child, handing it to me. So you do recognise me, I exclaim, there is a trail through the labyrinth after all. Glassy-eyed gaze into the distance. You called me by name! I blink and the child is gone. I turn and my wife is standing in the pergola, as though waiting for something, but staring past me. Why must you blank me. That's not true, she replies, I see you, I know very well you are there. I am momentarily cheered, then wonder whether the appearance of recognition may not be deceiving me; there is recognition but is it of me, specif-ically. Do we even inhabit the same time zone, or have the years between us decided to move in opposite directions, like continental shelves pulling apart. We each wind our watches in different directions, one forward one back, and pass each other by, passengers on separate trains, exchanging a knowing glance as we slip from the station in different directions.

§ 77

I am hunkering down in search of a book at my feet, then when I stand up experience a sudden rush of blood to the head. I cling to the bookshelf and notice there are phosphenes, small spots of light, dancing before my eyes. It is a sensation like nothing so much as vertigo at ground level. But I have often experienced gravity as a transforming force in this way. I write these remarks of an evening at my kitchen table, pushing the words around on the page, and frequently have the experience of giving up and rising to go to bed at eleven only to feel a rush of inspiration as I mount the stairs, sometimes to the point where I scribble notes on my hand in the hope that they and the inspiration behind them will still be there in the morning. But my notes-to-self tend to pall in the light of day, I have found. What is really going on is the adrenaline rush of separating myself from the task in hand, and the literal *esprit d'escalier* of realising over a late-night pee how much better upstairs-me, so different from his downstairs equivalent, could have managed the job. Were I to sit at the top of the stairs and seize the moment, I doubt if anything much would result. It is the blankness I find liberating, really. All around me my family are sleeping. Lines of bins are visible outside through my study window. Impeccably sensible family saloon cars stand in drives. Our semi-feral cat is sitting under a tree in the distance and may have noticed me in the window, even at this distance. Over my head is a hatch to the attic, a space I have visited maybe twice or thrice. As a child I slink off to our converted attic and stare out over the trees at nothing in particular, the king of domestic elevation. One day I find the bloodied corpse of a blackbird, where it has flown in the window and failed to exit again, dashing itself maladroitly against the glass. How quickly the brilliant feathers lose their sheen and the dead bird begins to resemble a poorly-stuffed toy, how lost the glassy eyes look without their brilliant beads of light. Now lying down beside my son I feel a hacking cough come on. Keen not to disturb him I haul myself out of bed and stand by the window. From this side of the house too, through the blinds, I see bins and cars. But now the cat is there as well, staring with murderous intentness from the fence. To the one who watches latest and last goes the victory. Human, your vigils out beyond the fringe of your daylight offend me. But I lack his freedoms, his presentness in the nourishing darkness. I write in, I cling to a present tense I scarcely inhabit, and when I sleep it races away over the hill, mocking me as it goes. I wake in the morning, read what I've written last night, feel a rush of blood to the head and have to stand up. In his monk's cell, St Fillan of Dochart possessed the gift of making his arm light up, to read by in his hermit dark. And now in my disorientation I see lights before my eyes, the beam once more of inspiration. Then I open the curtain and it is swamped by the daylight, and I must wait until last thing at night again for that dizzying radiance to show itself once more.

§ 78

As we drift on our endless circuit from village to village there
will often be not much going on. A Co-op here, a war memorial there, a rusting see-saw squeaking to itself in the breeze.
But something we do see a lot of are community halls, typically large and unadorned structures, but also mysteriously
underused. Occasionally there will be stakes in the ground by
the roadside advertising an upcoming meat raffle or boy scouts'
AGM. Otherwise their purpose remains rather vague. I think
of these spots, however, as I watch an engrossing short film of
Stornoway crooner Calum Kennedy's doomed tour of Scotland
in 1981. When I first come across it, I fancy I have stumbled on
Scotland's answer to *Spinal Tap*, a withering portrait of artistic
folly. But watching it again I decide it is closer to *A Mighty Wind*,
a genuine tribute to artistic single-mindedness (and folk music)
pursued in the face of an indifferent world. It is not without
mysterious aspects. The tour is a disaster. The group, com-
prising Calum himself and a retinue other musicians and light
entertainers, sheds members at an alarming rate for reasons of
alcoholic incapacity, shambolic management, and general loss
of the will to live. These losses of personnel are marked by the
narrator crossing the defectors' names off the tour poster. Is it a
set-up? Its farcical nature is what makes the tour so compelling,
but how did the film-makers know in advance this was going to
happen? Since, if they didn't, why make the film? As the tour
progresses and the merry troubadours make their way from
Thurso to the Western Isles, the venues downsize from concert
halls to community halls. Logically, the film should terminate
with Calum going door to door in North Uist asking to come

in and sing a few songs in people's front rooms. And now for the community halls of our dear region. I admire Calum's persistence in the face of such daunting odds – the scene in which he walks up and down on the pier after news of a ferry cancellation, head in hands, touches tragicomic levels of grandeur – and decide to recreate his tour with our little family band. The children play bagpipes and fiddle, dancing in circles as they do so. Their mother vamps chords on an out-of-tune piano, and I stride on stage for a belting rendition of *Brochan Lom*, a song about porridge: *Brochan lom, tana lom, brochan lom na sùghain.* The porridge is thin and made of sowans. We trace a great arc of community halls from the coast to the mountains: *Brochan lom, tana lom, brochan lom na sùghain.* Porridge still rather thin. Family members wander off and return, nobody comes to see us: *Brochan lom, tana lom, brochan lom na sùghain.* The porridge, do I make myself clear about the porridge. Crushed at last by my vainglory, I soliloquise disconsolately to camera. Ah then, so I too have believed all along that someone is watching! *Brochan lom 's e tana lom 's e brochan lom na sùghain.* Such is porridge, such is life. I have no regrets. I knew from the start what we were getting into. Given the chance I would do it all again.

§ 79

As we enjoy our morning porridge, which is of an entirely satisfactory texture thank you very much, one of the children is
paying close attention to the breakfast programme on Radio
3. Climbing onto the counter where we keep the radio, they
hunch reverently over the speakers and dials, while an extract
plays from Handel's *Jephtha*: 'Whatever is is right'. Striking
proposition, and one I believe Handel changed from 'Whatever God ordains is right'. It is the breakfast table, and hardly
the time for musical lectures, but since you ask, children (no one
has asked), here is a handy reminder of the difference between
Handel and Bach. By the end of his life Bach's dense fugal textures had become hopelessly old-fashioned. His work fell out of
the repertoire after his death, and had to be revived decades
later by Mendelssohn. Handel by contrast was a man in tune
with the spirit of the age, a brisk moderniser; someone who saw
the beefy colonial swagger of Regency England and sniffed an
opportunity. My vehemence on this topic is no doubt inflected
by the beefily self-assertive wrongness of our own times, children. Because whatever is is not right, no. All our lives we have
lived in a series of shadowlands deficient in conspicuous reality.
Do you think those Jacobite mists we chase around our pinky
castles are real, the giants asleep under the mountain? I mean
in their eyes, they, the other, the world. We are right but are
not the world. We are the world but they might dispute this.
They are wrong but are very tenacious. On it goes. Rightness
is opposition. What is is . . . define 'is'. Meeting a friend in the
street, Wittgenstein notices he is carrying some gramophone
records of, I think, Beethoven or Schubert. Are they any good?

asks the Austrian. That depends on what you mean by good, replies his friend. I mean exactly what you mean, says Wittgenstein. It becomes a kind of blinking competition. No we are not relativists, what we believe is the simple truth. But poetically so. It was a good tune, wasn't it, and no we can't have it again, that's not how the radio works. The Biblical story of Jephtha is a troubling one. Promising the Lord to sacrifice the first thing he sees on his triumphant return from battle, Jephtha meets his daughter, run to greet him. In Handel's *Jephtha* an angel intervenes to spare the child's life. In the Biblical version, the child, Iphis, is indeed put to death. But which version is right. Whatever is. Is disputed. Bach is better than Handel. Oh, but '*Ombra mai fu*' from Xerxes is simply exquisite. Undoubtedly. But Handel's is a post-fugal world; his heart is not in it when he writes counterpoint. A new world was coming. It hogs the light. After his death Bach's musical scores were used as wrapping paper, and his passions on the gospels of Luke and Mark were lost. There is a lost world and it is no less real than the one we inhabit. We are in and are not in the world. Define 'world'.

§ 80

Using the mapping function of a popular internet search engine
I revisit the village in the mountain region of my childhood
with which I began and learn surprisingly little. I see what an
irritant electricity powerlines are in the images that pop up,
and also how anything I might wish to inspect is off to the left
or right of the minor roads around which the map is arranged.
I prod helplessly at sights beyond the roadside hedges but they
belong to another realm. Equally, I can rotate on the spot but
not look up or down. I can deliver a parcel but not peer over
a wall in search of a wildflower. Life is presumed to follow a
line of rapacious vectors, locked onto their target and brook-
ing no distraction, and the past is less a living thing than the
subject of an enormous information retrieval project. In the
face of this, I therefore identify the following possibilities where
the actual past and not its simulacrum is concerned. The past,
or the event, happens once and once only, sealing itself in as
it does so. The event has happened, like a photographic slide
being selected with the press of a button, and we navigate forwards and backwards, towards or away from it, with our mental clickers. These images are discrete and any kinetic unity
they form − like figures in a flip book, or doodles in the corner
of a child's copy-book − is illusory, a mechanical accident. Or:
the event has happened, afloat on a living temporal stream in
which we swim against the tide to recapture it. Or: the event
has happened, in the living temporal stream, but is no more
moored in the eddies and flows than we are, so that we go
where we saw it last only to find it floating away in the other
direction. Or: the event has not yet fully happened. I open a

church door and see the window ahead of me and the experience continues to work itself out as I board a car ferry to cross the sea and trudge through snow at the top of a mountain. I place a child on my shoulders and skip down the lane and another facet of the stained-glass window comes into focus, not in memory but for the first time. I break my experience down into ever smaller units, in search of the indivisible instant, only to find there is none. Were there to be such a thing, the glass would shatter and fall from its frame. In this sense, one might even suggest that the experience has yet to so much as begin. One final possibility is that my experience of flow is so total as to have absorbed all possible versions of itself, and thus turned off any sense of continuity against which to measure that flow. The experience of stasis and flow, the one and the many – they paradoxically merge. Time does not flow, it teems. Like currents in the slowest of rivers the panels in the stained-glass window shimmer and glow, but secretly ripple and seethe, out of sight, like an anthill.

§ 81

I wonder if you can hear me. Hello hello. I am speaking to my parents via a video messaging program. Being older, they occupy that particular group for whom keeping up with technology represents both a victory and a perpetual small surprise, so there will be no messing around with jokey backgrounds or other such trickery. There is also a long delay with getting started, in which there is much talk of whether we can hear one another. Hello, hello again. I think you have your mic off. Now it's on but your picture's off. This all sounds quite comical, but is as nothing compared to my attempts to deal with telephone calls, which I gave up many years ago now. One of them would speak, followed by a pause, into which I would attempt to speak only for the other to start speaking at that moment. Or some other permutation, end result deadlock. It strikes me the landline telephone is the technology with which my parents and their generation coincide most closely, after which people of my generation have drifted off into first email, then text messaging, then whatever this is we are using today, but half-heartedly: vaguely annoyed at my parents' inability to master it too, but without any great belief in it myself. My parents are sitting in what looks like semi-darkness, the tops of their heads and their eyes drifting in and out of shot. Could I get the children to sit in front of the screen. I suspect not. Today we were in the mountains, my father says. We passed that war memorial Beckett mentions. But I myself have brought my parents to this monument several years ago, on a Sunday drive. I notice in my chats how they they will sometimes, as now, present me with an aspect of home much as they might to the child of an English cousin visiting the old country for the first time. Is it a form of self-exoticisation, the landscape of home become an object of tourist consumption now, rather than this or that fixture I might cycle up the road to visit before free-wheeling home and slumping onto the sofa to watch the news in my parents' company, wine glasses in hand all round. We saw this painting by Jack Yeats, we visited the writers' museum. Sounds lovely, I must visit sometime. But now my parents are having some work done to the house and my mother sends me photo after photo of piles of old books and magazines asking which of them she can get rid of. How about that book about the mountains, do you still need it. But does she mean need it here or there. If I was there I could just go there – that other 'there' – read it, then go there. If it was here I could read it before going over, if I was going. Or read it then not go. Or neither. The mountains. Are they still there, throwing their shadow over the garden at dusk, over the bookshelf where the book about them stands waiting, unread. Sorry, does that answer your question.

§ 82

When it first occurred to me to keep these notes on my experiences I found a pen and scribbled 'Because a fire was in my head' from W. B. Yeats's 'The Song of Wandering Aengus' on my hand, a writing pad I have used with some regularity since becoming a parent. What fire, though. Did Yeats's wandering Aengus feel overcome by rushes of blood to the head when bouts of anxiety or other dysfunction got a bit much for him. I wonder. Yeats was not the most neurodiversely sensitive of poets. He had his dyslexia but then he had his eugenicist side too, with all that hateful blether about the 'uneducatable masses' and what to do with them. When I teach Yeats I notice students find him tricky to get the measure of. They tend to take him at face value, and see a big-house aristocrat, for instance, rather than a bourgeois bohemian trying it on; they need careful coaching in what one might term the fantasy element of his narratives. Students reading poetry today will often reach for concepts of sex, gender and race, but if that seems too present-centred, good luck reconstructing Yeats's exact historical perspective for your students to enter instead. I therefore feel little compunction about writing (on my hand) the words 'Because a fire was in my head' and viewing it as a small commentary on the flare of neurodivergence burning through my own thought-processes. Like me, Aengus didn't like talking in staff meetings and spent his time, head bowed, drawing elaborate doodles instead. He lived in a tower-block but chose to see his surroundings as an untouched natural landscape, free of the pollution that played such havoc with his asthma. The stuff about trout is a metaphor for artistic self-expression in the face of neurodivergence.

Having initially seen it as a challenge he decided to embrace it as a kind of superpower. It added spice to his line breaks in particular, he thought. As for the woman he mentions, who knows. I read Yeats's poem and strongly visualise, by way of a landscape, a young man lying on a chaise longue in London. There is talk in 'Who Goes With Fergus' of the warriors of old Ireland flitting round the place in their chariots, yet strangely enough no archaeological evidence of these vehicles has ever been found. It's probably code for synaesthesia or something. A great mistake with Yeats I find is to take anything he takes as a normative statement of the true-or-false kind. 'The best lack all conviction, while the worst / are full of passionate intensity' in 'The Second Coming', for instance. Why do the best lack all conviction? No they don't. Are you having me on? This poem has become wildly popular in recent years with newspaper columnists in search of something resonant to say about geopolitics, but I don't see it myself. I dislike the rise of authoritarian politics but should enjoy the feeling of how evil they are rather than do anything about it, for some reason. Oh so you think poems are ways of fighting back against bad politics do you, can you list some of your successes on that score for me. Sorry, that's not how poetry works. It is its own victory. Anything else is a bonus but not something I can budget for. But we're wandering off-topic here. Sorry, I have to go to my hazel wood now. Because a fire is in my head.

§ 83

I write these notes first on my hand, then transfer them to scraps of paper, and eventually onto this file. I have written in the present tense, but with no sense of when that will translate into the present tense in which you (anyone) might read this text. But why the presumption of transmission and successful reception, I wonder, if that has indeed been my underlying assumption. There was a time when people wrote things designed to be secret. Emily Dickinson sewed her unread poems into pillowcases. And now is as good a time as any to record that many of my notes era nekat ni eht mrof fo 'sdrawkcab' – are taken in the form of 'backwards', in homage to one of the my few natural talents, hcihw si eht ytiliba ot klat, sey, sdrawkcab – which is the ability to talk, yes, backwards. Some explanatory notes. I do this phonetically. The 'sdrawkcab' (backwards) for 'fire' may be written 'erif', but is pronounced 'ryaf' (mind that diphthong) (I will not trouble you here with the phonetic alphabet). Sdrawkcab can be spoken on a word-by-word basis, or alternatively the whole sentence can be inverted. I'm fine with either. My natural aptitude for this I put down to my being left-handed, and not predisposed to treat left-to-right as the natural order of things other people take it to be. The 'sdrawkcab' option is for me like captions on a foreign film, a permanently scrolling translation of what I am hearing the 'right' way round in my daily life. A comparison would be to a family language left behind several generations ago in the old country. Norwegian, let's say. Great-great-grandfather Pedersen was a reindeer herder from Tromso. No one since then has spoken Norwegian. Except you: you pass every last thought you have

through an instant Norwegian filter, then back into English –
and also, no one is aware of this fact; you yourself are hardly
aware of this fact. When writing in this form, I do so from
right to left. Why though. To what end. What is really going
on here? Is this a language, a pidgin, a cant, a sub-language?
I have never met anyone else who talks 'sdrawkcab'. Were I to
do so I'm not sure how I might react. Would we talk it together?
Perhaps I would resent the thought of a fellow sdrawkcab-er
and conceal or dissemble my ability. Reading this text back,
however, with an awareness of where it has been, linguistically,
I am forced to pause on the assumption that this final version is
its correct destination. What is through the stained-glass window of the text. Let's go through and see. Or maybe let's not. I
can decipher the notes I took while thinking about it and spell
out what it all meant. And suppose what it meant was indecipherable, or the indecipherable was what it meant. Elbarehpic-
edni. Are you with me, are you keeping up. Not too late to turn
round and try again. Back is on and on is back. I am cycling
through the mountains in the region of my birth when I notice
an unusual church in what I take to be a New Mexican style. I
would go in, but I'm not sure where it might lead.

§ 84

I have therefore wondered whether the experiences I have described here have not been essentially private and unsusceptible to wider communication – whether I haven't been, perhaps, speaking an essentially secret language all along. I use words thinking I know what they mean, whereas in reality I am moving around small private tokens within my own phantasmagoria. But I have come to reject this suggestion. If you asked me for a pancake and I gave you one, you might wonder what the mystery object I had handed you was. That's not a pancake, you'd think, of the buttery abominations they eat around here, unless you too live in these parts. But have I been extrapolating from my local differences to a fixed but false external standard against which I am judged and found wanting? Mrs McGillivray down the road would call that a pancake, it's not as though I've handed you a lump of coal. You say 'window' and mean something you open or close to admit or exclude the breeze, or so I imagine. I say 'window' and am stopping my bicycle to enter an unusual-looking church in the mountainous region of my youth, where I am taken aback by the stained-glass window behind the altar, that church, that window, not the thing in front of my desk here, no. But is your window really so simple, maybe you stand opening and closing it for hours at a time, remembering the gusts of wind that played in your hair in your childhood, whole narratives I cannot possibly be expected to know. The mere window, the thing you open and close, comes freighted with all the stories you want, that's part of the deal. So when I talk about private experiences, I mean a style of signalling, a way of eating my pancake and flapping my

167

arms and saying, do you see this, do you see what I'm doing? You couldn't possibly know what this is, yes pancakes are more buttery here than elsewhere, but this goes beyond that, you've no idea, simpleton that you are. But maybe you see very well what I'm doing, in my melodramatic way, and think, what's the drama here, this is pancakes we're talking about here, not Fermat's last theorem. And so in a way everyone is happy, with the theatre of it all. The world is full of people shouting their incommunicable privacies, their 'whereof we cannot speak's, but who put put me in charge of what can and can't be said. Thereof we must. Be silent. The concept of a private language then: rejected. Do you, reader, get it, how I feel dragging my knuckles along the wall of the quay back home that time until they bled, cursing God and man as I do, what's that all about. Yes of course you do. I have my say and you listen and nothing is lost. And what do you take it to mean? Exactly what I do. Will the youngsters be wanting their pancakes with that. Yes, they will will thanks. And some cinnamon on the coffee. Pancakes, children, lovely pancakes. Thank you for listening.

§ 85

Is there a lift? asks the child when told we are off to the garden centre. Is there a lift? they similarly ask of the park, the beach, the mountain. It is their 'Is it about a bicycle'. And there is a lift, sometimes, or in the garden centre at least. There's a lift, Daddy, it's an Otis, you press the button, you have to press it, and we go up, we're going up, there's a sheave and a counterweight too, as we go up they go down, look we've arrived, we're not getting out, we're going down now, I'll press the button. I meet a friend in the lobby of a hotel in a distant town and the child helpfully pipes up that there is a lift: we can go in it; get in the lift now, press the button, we're going up. Would you mind terribly going back down again, I ask my friend, maybe running around a bit in the lobby with us, then coming back up; no, not at all. Thank you. There is a lift, Daddy. Yes there is. Strangely enough the lift is entered by a member for parliament, no less, albeit for a more than usually repellent party, will he toss some chat in the direction of the arm-flapping child, thankfully not. In the car one day I turn on the radio and the topic of the phone-in show is why we love cruises. Why do we love cruises, I mean lifts, why do we love lifts so much, it's just something we're passionate about, as a family. What is normal to you is strange to us, what is strange to you is normal to us. There is a counterweight, there is always a counterweight. It counterbalances the load borne by the lift, relieving the motor. In a fugue there is always a countersubject coming along on the heels of the subject, going one way when the subject goes the other, but then there is stretto too, when the countersubject turns up before the subject has finished, and the melodic line is speaking over itself, in different time values, the one become many, everything divided into itself, what a glorious mess. On the lift's journey lift and counterweight pass: I see the counterweight whizz by, but keep your finger on the button, Daddy, we have to keep going. Yet sometimes as now the lift will unaccountably stop. In Curry's, a few feet short of the first floor and in sight of the rows of washing machines our child had hoped to inspect. But what if there were a lift inside the lift, could we take that and keep going, on our travels of the imagination, good idea, we open the doors and go in and press the button. I have vivid memories of an astronomical clock I saw once with dials within dials, the hands on the largest clock moving slowly in one direction and the hands on another inside it more quickly in the opposite direction, and watching it I felt time transformed, and up we go in our stationary lift, nearly there now, if we go any faster we risk losing all sense of movement.

§ 86

Seasick on dry land I am seasick too by the sea, among the fisherfolk's cottages where passing prows tower over roofs and the mermaids in the basement come out to look at me. Proximity to the sea means you must sit outside in fine weather, it is the law, with sand in your chips and mystery dogs approaching you, tennis balls held tight in their jaws. Half a mile inland this would be madness, perhaps it is madness here too. Inhabiting one of these cottages means you will talk to passers-by and be in and out of your neighbour's house all day, that too is the law. And what is the sea to the cat on the wall, does she lift a paw to its waves and say, thus far and no further. My eye drawn by a line of maritime gewgaws, I gaze at one of the cottage windows but see a further window framed within it, split in two by the sea and the sky and with in the far corner a container ship sailing off to the edge of the world. But where have I seen this before, could it have been through a porthole on that other boat on that other journey, sailing here, so many years ago now. And what do they see, today's sailors out on the waves, looking back at us gazing impotently after them. There will always be a cluster of boats when we come here, off to the north, waiting beyond the wind turbines for the tide of the market to change before they bring their cargo ashore, their floating lochs of oil on water, and their Filipino or Malaysian crew staring out at night at the lights on the coastline, these very lights here. What I have sought is an entry point into an ultimate beyond, is this so much to ask. Would you care to dance for the sea, children. You would and you do, by the skeleton sunk in the sand, with backbone and legs. A sea dragon.

Awaiting its evolutionary moment, passing us in the opposite direction while we re-enter the waves. Today's boats in the harbour include the *Edda Frenda*, the *Hjaltland*, the *Skandi Aukra* and the *Hermit Power*, we shall sport in their backwash, in a low tide haloed by plovers and turnstones. And where the giant Viking's face passes on the side of the ferry, I fashion from shingle a shelter against dark thoughts rising, the sea-dark cave of the soul, defy doom for riches – who's with me? Who, breasting waves to grim-dree their weird will plunge into star-crossed eel pools, follow where my ripples smooth over? And it washes over me, this vector of fancy I have tossed like a guy rope into the waves, and is gone and away we turn, with behind us the stick I have used to inscribe your names, children, left upright in the sand. All the way home it remains in the corner of perception, that moment when with a mighty look at me the sea withdrew, the curtains drawn on the waves and the curtains drawn on the curtains drawn on the waves, and our dropped chips blowing off over the dunes.

§ 87

But even as I depart I lag behind myself and dig my heels in, this territory mine now, not to be surrendered. A man called forwards, who changed his name to sdrawkcab, has come to a seaside town intending to kill his future self. He has moved to a cottage with a view of the sea, and of an out-of-season morning sits counting the drops of spray nosing their way down the glass. There are no trinkets in his windows. A death has occurred in the hedgerow, he glimpses some quick thing poking around in it. Keep your children away from his door. A week, a year, a decade, spent in an alien town, averting his gaze from the neighbours he passes in the street, the run-off of their high-spirited laughter leaking through the walls of his bedroom at night, he hears them, knows what they're laughing at. The world of the unhappy man is not the same world as that of the happy man. Some days sdrawkcab catches sight of his quarry at the end of the street, between the gable ends with the quayside storage tanks behind him, carrying a mannequin as he goes. It is colourfully dressed and made up, and jabbers away to the man, perhaps with a voicebox on a string, the better to give him an illusion of company, an illusion of life. Through a gap in the curtain sdrawkcab sees the illuminated birthday cake of the Victorian ballroom, the couples making their way there of an evening, and then the sordid eight-limbed spiders they form, wriggling on the rocks as they spill out in the late twilight, the sky still streaked with sun at eleven. He feels that he is alone. And there is his quarry again now, eyes moist with the filthy promise of company-keeping. sdrawkcab clutches at the lace curtain, his mind a necropolis of vindications, a roof full of loose slates falling one at a time into the gutter below. Who's the woman, sdrawkcab will hiss when he catches up with his quarry at last, found someone willing to put up with you at last then have you, she doesn't know you like I do. Then reaching for something inside his greatcoat he lunges at him but – but in reality it is I who have killed sdrawkcab and left him in a pool behind me at the seaside. We have been to the seaside and had a lovely time. It reminded me of home, home-home, rather than where we live now. There, that wasn't too hard, was it. At any given stage I am aware of forming and shedding these chrysalis selves, become their own shrouds where they fall. Theirs is a bitter truth. This too is a chrysalis self and will fall to the ground without a butterfly. 'We have been to the seaside . . . it reminded me of home'! Who am I kidding. The waves have been turned off, there is no seaside, the mannequin is me, dropped on the rocks and grinning to itself the inane grin of the unassuageable. Idea for going beyond forwards and backwards, sdrawrof and sdrawkcab, would be to talk only in palindromes. I did, did I? Don't nod. Was it a cat I saw?

§ 88

One more time the sensation of everything happening all at once: Ligeti's *Atmosphères* on the car stereo, a piece that appears to trade melodic progression for a sheer wall of sound, hanging monstrously in the air. There is no background or foreground, only sheets of micropolyphony sliding with infinite slowness one over the other. And yet it moves, or does all move around it while it stays still, or is it all of everything at once, stasis and motion combined. That one again, Daddy. Everything happening all at once all over again. So that: the land of my birth is grey, green and brown, I say, up to my ankles in muck, but look, I spy a patch of brilliant red and blue over there, in that window, and another here in an island of glass, in the city. If I grind my teeth exactly like – so – that means I am playing the countersubject of a Bach fugue while the bus brakes as it rounds the corner in the street outside, now, now and now. When the last lorry rolls onto the ferry, the bows fall back into place and my father uses the phrase 'tickety boo' or 'the whole shebang' and the steel stairs I climb echo harshly under the heel of my boots. The lorry drivers load up on lager in the Sportsman Bar but then drive off tomorrow morning on four or five hours' sleep. A little-known fact about that house in the middle of the motorway is that people think the farmer refused to sell and stayed out of sheer contrariness, whereas actually . . . but I don't know that yet, I will later, but move it around in the pattern now because – but what is this pattern, am I reeling this off in some manner of sequence now? There is a sequence, there is a sequence of sequences, arranged in chronological and reverse chronological order, arranging in alphabetical order the names of the last butterfly species to fly through the window or the names of the nearest mountain summits visible above the line of houses or trees. In the back seat one child is listing every last lift they have travelled in, all of them bobbing up and down in memory like rubber ducks in the bath, and the other is performing Rossini's duet for two cats, taking both parts. There are no children yet, I am on a daytrip to the mountain with my parents, my wife is trudging up a long hill with her mother and the shopping in a string bag. There is no four of us, there is a sequence of fours of us, stretching lazily off to the spatial and temporal horizons, and arranged by . . . Wait, that's too much, slow down: no kicking please, stop that now. It does get quite noisy though, yes, maybe turn it off for now. But what do people fancy listening to instead. And what did you want to do for our next adventure. Nothing, announces the younger child, peremptorily and we sit in our moving stasis feeling it all happen, that glorious absence.

§ 89

What is a repetition, I ask myself abstractly, what has it all meant, then realise I have left the child's coat and hat in the park. We will have to go back. A rather large park, with at least three playgrounds. There is the playground with the steamroller, the playground with the giant slide, and the playground with the sand and the trains on the bridge overhead. You can sit in the steamroller and use it to flatten things, Daddy, straight like a pancake. Could you use it to flatten a pancake? Yes you could. Let's go the park then like we did yesterday. Look, there are three playgrounds, one with a steamroller, one with a giant slide, and one with sand and trains on a bridge overhead. Is the giant slide so big you could have a slide inside the slide? Yes Daddy, we should go down it, the slide in the slide. There is an installation to mark the local stone-cutting tradition, and here is a large stone from our village, with its name carved on it. Not just a stone then, but a stone squared, a stone labelled 'stone'. In the playground with the sand I watch the children immerse themselves while trains glide over the bridge, including perhaps the mail train that brings me a letter – there, I see it flutter past now – from the United States, describing the view from a train of 'These British fields straight out of British poetry, / bucolic green and stunningly mediocre.' It is a poem about Andrew Marvell, to whom views from train windows were an unknown pleasure, but whose canny eye looked out over the drains and marshes among which I once lived and made of them mythological landscapes, which then became more real than the things themselves, in which sense he invented them, the actual drains and marshes. I by the tide of. Am I repeating myself. We have come back to the park for the forgotten coat and hat which to my pleasure I find where I left them. Marvell praised Milton, 'albeit via oxymoron / ("understanding blind"), as England's supreme / gardener.' He also wrote blind of 'The Bermudas', that 'isle so long unknown / And yet far kinder than our own.' But one need not never have been somewhere to write of it blind. I might declare this imaginative terra incognita mine; or it might take possession of me, I place myself at its disposal; or no sooner gained than I might make sure to lose it again. Perhaps this has been my approach here, all along. In the letter my correspondent's train stops and Edward Thomas is suddenly at hand in his own stopped train, as though on the next platform. Will we leave my coat and hat behind again Daddy so we can come back tomorrow, yes let's. Why do I ever go anywhere except in search of what I have left behind. In all kinds of ways it's as though I've never been here before. And when we come back tomorrow the coat and hat will be gone. One train approaches another on the bridge, the here and the elsewhere, the past and the present, and they slow down to pass, that's the convention, though why, it's not as though they're about to touch, not as though they're about smash into each other.

§ 90

But trains do bump into things and find their urgent vectors this way and that crudely interrupted. There has been torrential rain and flooding and a train south is unable to proceed. Travelling back whence it came it encounters a landslip at speed, leaves the track, and three people are killed. A woman exits the wreckage and, unable to get a telephone signal, walks three miles along the track to raise the alarm. As the driver had previously passed the site of the landslip without incident, and was travelling in the opposite direction from a known hazard, perhaps there was an unconscious assumption of safety. The language for describing accidents of this kind tends to the bureaucratic ('without incident', 'raise the alarm'), and passing as I regularly do a roadside shrine to a car-crash victim – a football scarf and a faded bouquet tied to a tree-trunk – I feel aware of the terrible impotence of attempts to go beyond this, in any public way at least. Among the grim thoughts that occur on the rail crash is relief that the accident was not on the nearby Tay Bridge, with all the obligatory parallels this would have raised to McGonagall's poem on the Tay Bridge disaster. It continues to rain and the village is briefly cut off, in one direction at least. There is a drain by a turn in the road where the water doesn't clear and forms a great loch, swiftly promoted to a mirror of ice, then lost under snow. We sit in the village café and looking out the window all I can see is the whiteout. With the great gusts of wind it has the appearance of coming straight at me. A farmer has taken his tractor out to help clear the roads and left his dog in the cab while he visits the shop, much to the amusement of our children, convinced it is the dog who is driving. Something you see in these conditions is cars skidding gently round corners or into parking spots, and even bumping up against things without it, somehow, being a problem. It's as though the gravitational force in the village has changed, or we have made alternative planetary arrangements, transplanting ourselves to the moon. I think of *Space: 1999*, that more suburban version of *Solaris* that exercised such fascination for me in the 1970s, and whose spaceships were, as I recall, forever bumping into things. A colony has been founded on the moon, whose nuclear waste dump then explodes, detaching the moon from the earth's orbit and sending it on its way through space. Soon it finds itself on a collision course with other planetary bodies, leaving the occupants of the moonbase (the Alphans) confused and divided as to what evasive action they might take. Gripped by madness, as his fellow Alphans think, Captain Koenig decides to allow the collision to occur. Several plot twists later the moment of impact arrives, only for the planet Atheria to disappear as though nothing has happened, and the moon sails on unharmed.

§ 91

Are you a dragon now, I ask a child bearing down on me in a bright red costume. No Daddy, I'm a human being eaten by a dragon. Can't you see. My wife sends me to the car to retrieve a left-behind object and tells me it is at her feet, by which she means where her feet would go in the car, not her feet here and now in the house. But that's understood. Where I'm from the buses are orange, I tell a curious child, meaning the 1980s rather than the place of my birth. Who knows what colour the buses are now in the place of my birth. But then I mention to my mother about another book in her house and tell her it's in my room. In my room on the right where I sit at the computer. Make sure to knock before you go in. Observing Wittgenstein in the corner of a field, grunting to himself as he traced lines in the soil with a stick, a Mayo farmer assumed he was mad. He was drawing the duck-rabbit illusion: not so much a duck and a rabbit as an 'I see a duck' and an 'I see a rabbit'. But what was the actual thing that he saw. An 'I see a duck and I see a rabbit'. Pareidolia is the reinterpretation of objects in the visual field as familiar objects, bringing them into line with the comfortingly everyday, as when a rock on Mars appears to be in the shape of a human face. But there should be an opposite of pareidolia, as when someone says something familiar and I hear something entirely other: for 'Yorkshire' for instance, the Irish '*dhearcadh siar*', 'a backwards look'. I retranslate or back-translate, since what we are given is always already a translation of some kind, and usually a poor one. I attempt to type a phone message not in English only to find my phone knows better than I what I'm trying to say and is here to help me with that ('my hovercraft

181

is full of eels'). Curse it anyway. If musical scores came with a built-in autopredict in the early twentieth century, twelve-tone music would have been straightened out into Yankee Doodle and never occurred. D. H. Lawrence died in Venice. No, he died in Vence, in the south of France, but this fact is almost impossible to state in print without it being hyper-corrected to Venice. So perhaps in reality that is where he died, now. Life runs on tram lines. But the tram is not free to leave the tram line, if it does so something very bad will have happened. But the tram lines are not set up for my convenience, I find, all my life I have felt this. But do they still have those what are they called you pull when you want to get off. Communication cords. And what colour are the trams where you are from. I spent the 1980s tripping over tram lines in the street but the trams themselves had disappeared long before my birth. Then twenty years later, once I'd cleared out, they came back. How should I know what colour they are.

§ 92

Going upstairs to write in the depths of winter, I inaccurately line up a pillow against the steel bedposts before climbing under the duvet. The bars at the bedhead jab uncomfortably into my back, but twenty minutes later of pawing away at the keyboard I haven't changed posture. Unlike the cat on the gentle promontory of my knees, I would seem to struggle with putting myself at ease. No masochist, it's more that I am insensitive and haven't noticed. Lying there thumbing through some new books scattered round, one thing I have noticed is their long and heartfelt acknowledgement sections. Thank you to so-and-so for all of your. With endless gratitude to my for your. I watch new books tuck themselves under their covers and claim their welcoming space, where once books were spat out without much ceremony, to lie where they fell. Is it comfort though, or pained self-exposure, this space they claim. The world is harsh; only restatement of our mutual dependency can face down its huge indifference. But then I remember the vapid encomia authors once felt obliged to direct at their patrons, moneyed know-nothings that they often were. With somewhere between these poles the merely unattached text, born of nothing and the property of no one. The only dedicatee of any of James Joyce's works was his soul, in an early and now-lost play. Harriet Shaw Weaver gave him all that money and where was her thank-you. But I am wary of this discussion, lest I be seen to confuse my safe and conventional position with any manner of outlaw status (it is rather cold, but I also have the radiator on). So perhaps it's best not to raise the subject at all, to avoid misunderstanding. Though it's true, these notes have signed no social contract, have no reader waiting. The question remains, then, of how one occupies cultural space. Radnóti's poems entered the mass grave with him where he fell. The modern French novels on the shelf at my bedside have no cover images or biographical notes. Writers of this period worshipped an idol of autonomy, future generations will decide, and paid it homage with their talk of unbeholden works, born of nothing and dedicated to no one. Literally no one read them. Thank you for listening, language. Often I have approached the letters of the alphabet as one might a group of acquaintances in the school playground unsure if they would give me the time of day or edge away dismissively. If I find the bars at the bedhead so uncomfortable I can always move. The cat here half an hour ago is now outside on the window ledge, unsure whether it wants to come in or stay out. If I was truly alone, that condition would represent something more than a posture or style. Thanks to my nothing and no one, my gushing dedication could run, companions of a lifetime. If we are connected we are connected whether these words reach you or not. As I type a child enters the room and, seeing what I am doing, writing a passage in fact about that very child, slams the laptop shut.

§ 93

We are walking by the river one day when we notice a house
we have passed many times from the front, on the road, is
open at the rear. A panel is missing from its back door, so I
make my way in. For somewhere that appears to have last been
inhabited sometime in the 1970s the interior is looking well
preserved. A number of expensive sinks and fireplaces remain
in place and a child's bedroom is covered in wallpaper dec-
orated with gypsy caravans. From the window I see my wife
and children skip over the uneven ground with our distinctive
five-pointed mountain dominating the landscape behind them.
An oddity of Tarkovsky's *Mirror*, a film with its own version of
time-travel across decades, is that he casts the same actress as
Alexei's mother (in youth) and ex-wife, while the director's real-
life mother also features as Alexei's ex-wife in old age, and the
director's wife plays that character's neighbour. If this seems
odd it is probably no more so than the film's shifts between
dream and reality so if we can handle those, then why not that
too. Calling Tarkovsky's work haunting is probably a shade on
the trite side, given the vivid and even overwhelming sense it
creates of these people, past or dead, being present, in the here
and now. I have been in many abandoned houses in these parts,
including, further up in the mountains, those of World War
One soldiers who left home and did not return, and the element
I would stress is less their hauntedness than their habitability.
Here is a large pile of *Evening Expresses* nearly half a century old,
to go with my mildewing piles of old *TLS*s under the bed at
home, and I after all am half a century old myself. Though our
house is indistinguishable on the outside from those around it,

my impractical side has guaranteed enough low-level disrepair to put us well on the road to what I am experiencing now. Were either of the children to turn around now and meet my gaze, then remember this moment years from now, they would most likely think of it as their father in the house, in 'our' house, even, rather than their father framed by a cut-off and unrecoverable past – someone else's unrecoverable past that is, rather than – oh, you know what I mean! How long can we carry these worlds within worlds without them all folding back into one. It is May but one of the children is carrying a snow globe, which they stop and shake. Without being shaken upside down to produce its out-of-season whiteout, the house in the globe falls short of itself and its role, its destiny even. Take and invert the scene I am painting. Now watch it reassemble through that cloud of distortion. Are we back yet, the house, the window with my face in it, the floorboards sufficiently settled for me to clamber over, before I descend the gapped stairs to cross the field to where my wife and children wait by the river and everything flows and stands still.

§ 94

You, lost in the dark somewhere near-but-far-from-me as I write these notes, like Nessie Dunsmuir while her husband Sydney stayed up late composing in the same room. You in the light through the blinds beside me some other time and the blind maggots of our tongues interlocked. Mise-en-scène as the occasion requires. Or in a darkness shared, some other time again, me biting my tongue, perhaps aspiring to swallow whole the passionate transitory and succeeding only in sinking my teeth in myself. How does the one connect to the other, past to present. Hold me, I said. I splice these cinematic rushes together and then the image wheel snags and fails to proceed. All this time I have seen the window of light in the dark and passed through it, presuming you have done too, beside me in that gloom. But what if not. Why presume the light will continue, the dark not drag it down and consume it. I want that moment alive to my touch, only let it form within my hands once more. And so the commemorative itch, the need to take bodily hold of the past. Is sex writing. Is writing sex. To think that stimulation to the correct degree of the organ of sex will produce all the effects of tumescence, with the attendant risk of overflow: remarkable. Lurid blooms in the image world's nightgarden, seeded in their soil of implacable need. There is a passage somewhere in Jean Genet where he describes writing a letter from prison with his penis. The average ejaculation contains anything from 40 million to 1.2 billion sperm. Reaching the back wall of the cervix sperms will make a decision to turn left or right. Writing might begin with sketches, notes made on whatever's to hand, my own hand. When ready one finds a surface to inscribe. Prepares an agreed instrument. Establishes a sense of connection where we lean in at that point of encounter. I have found myself in my time composing lines of poetry at night and been reduced to writing them down in the dark, sometimes on skin, illegible the next morning. Tell me what traces you wake up to though, or if none where have they gone. Traces of past selves into which the body extends, stretching splay-legged under the sheets. Lie on my side and it is that time we lay thus in the ferry, pressed tight against the wall. Roll around onto my belly and it is that other time in the woods. Roll back around and it is a future time of which I as yet know nothing, into which an empty palm reaches and grips. Consider the sense of sorrowful blankness after evacuation. Now consider it envisaged from before that moment. Best perhaps head it off in advance. Best just not. A drizzle of sublimation drenches over the brain and drains into, mixes with, memory. A mole on your inside thigh, my teeth inching lazily over your ear and neck, as though offered up in the darkness for this purpose alone. Is sex. Writing. These words sent out to fuck a void. Are you there. Hold me. But enough of these notes for now. Time for bed.

§ 95

From where I sit I see Venus rising, a planet I have seen many another winter evening occupy that far low corner of the sky. Then to my surprise I am told I am looking at Jupiter and Saturn in conjunction. I take this information on trust, without quite banishing the suspicion that I am watching some entirely other heavenly body. But assurances have been made, and the experience – real or not – feels earned. Staring at the heavens, as was his wont, Kepler believed that musical harmony mirrored the movements of the planets, and that the orbits of celestial bodies made music which, while apparently inaudible, could be heard by the soul. Kepler's cosmology contained six planets; the model of their orbits he inherited from Copernicus still showed them following perfect circles round the sun. After much study he realised these orbits followed an elliptical, not circular path. The existence of the further-out planets eluded Kepler, though when Neptune was discovered it was thanks as much to an absence as to anything actually there. Gravity-induced disturbances in the orbit of Uranus meant that planet was not always where it should have been, and the object causing them could only have been, not Neptune the star (as it was still believed to be), but Neptune the planet. Am I getting that right? I am reminded therefore that objects I look at may not be what I take them to be, and that to find what I seek I may have to stare into gaps, holes, 'absences, darkness, death: things which are not'. But what do I seek. Among the more unusual skills I picked up in the music college of my long-ago youth is the composition of vocal music in the style of pre-Baroque composers such as Palestrina. The rules for this style are hopelessly ornate and, to all but the trained ear, inaudible. Do not let two voices leap to a perfect interval unless one of them is an inner part. One perfect interval can follow another in the same voices only if one of the voices moves stepwise. There was an edge of not just aesthetic but theological disapproval to getting things wrong, as with the use of the diminished fifth, or 'devil in music'. One composer of this period famous for his audacious use of dissonances is Gesualdo. If people know anything about Gesualdo it is that, finding her *in flagrante*, he murdered his wife and her lover. He was not charged with any offence. Is his daring chromatic style a coded expression of remorse, or at least of psychological extremity? In so far as people even hear it today, hear it as any different from Palestrina, this being after all a rather niche musical interest these days. I stare up at the Jupiter-Saturn conjunction, in so far as it is distinguishable from Venus or some bright-burning star. But then when I check again the following week it is gone and my mistaking of one thing for another has become much of a muchness, whatever I saw, and I give up my glance to that dark, in which they all shelter, unseen, and I too, in my way, gathered into that inaudible music.

§ 96

There arises the question of my grave. In the event of my death I will be buried in the village by my wife and children, and a plain headstone erected, preferably indicating only my name and dates. No funerary flourishes required. There is one grave I pause at that reads simply 'Mother's grave'. Whose mother is that. Ah, but they know. Ours is a small village, and my family will be able to visit my grave regularly, daily if they wish. My extended family will be inconvenienced by the distance to travel, whether for my interment or future courtesy visits to my headstone, but where my immediate family are concerned perhaps the proximity to my grave will become an inconvenience of its own. To pass my grave on a quick trip to the Co-op for bananas, or on an evening dash to catch the post – how could this not grow into a burden or even an embarrassment. Assuming, that is, my family choose to stay in the village, which they may not. My children will scatter, my widow remarry, their minds will wander, and rightly so. Perhaps therefore my grave is destined for moss-clad neglect and eventual toppling at the hands of hormonal youths, awkwardly fumbling among the tombs, far from parental eyes. In which case, why satisfy the minimal expectation of burial in the village graveyard, rather than in a disused cemetery on a mountainside or some other out-of-the way hole in the earth more in keeping with my itch for self-subtraction, subtraction from scenes of human intercourse, even of the post-mortem kind. These things can be arranged. Or might that be interpreted as a form of display, a show of defiance or flamboyance. Perhaps then merely walk into the woods or up the mountain and never come out, or

down, wedging myself between two great stones and skeletal-
ising at my leisure, up close with the pine martens at last, as
craved for so long, should this arrangement be preferred. Here
is every possible provision for the accommodation of dust. No
plans have been made for the disposal of my papers, or the
retrieval of this report from aged laptop or print-outs stuffed
down the back of a filing cabinet. As I have written about the
village and life here, there is I suspect a subcurrent of distance,
assuming as I have worked that I am talking to a reader far
from here and now, and whose remoteness will form our paradoxical point of connection. I even imagine them as the final
portal through whom this tale might pass, onwards, outwards
and free of its author at last. But I see now I am more likely to
be turned back on myself in a posthumous silence, my papers
neglected, dispersed, destroyed. So perhaps it is best to proceed
on that assumption, that the portal may be less portal than
frame, and what it frames less a way through than a fated dead-
end. Sacrilegious thought. One elegant solution to the pain of
this realisation would be to have my papers buried with me,
for perusal at my leisure. I write in the present tense. In which
tense are your reading me? Your doing so at all means which
of the above-sketched outcomes, I wonder. Reach out a hand.
What do you touch? Whose face is that in the dark? How close
are the walls? Don't answer that. Or not yet. Now turn the
page.

§ 97

So much of life is the art of converting the random into the pre-ordained, a football that bounces off my head into the back of the net for my cup-winning goal without my noticing. I have sculpted the heatmap of my wanderings into an epic of the inevitable. But fate will only take me so far. I look at the landscape here and see a colour chart rising as the eye lifts from green, yellow and purple, to brown and black, then white. All my life I have dreamed of ascending to the last zone, in Iceland perhaps, a country I suspect I will never visit, 'where from the Jokuls to the strand /The dimmed eye turns from smoke to steam'. After my death, my wife long settled into widhowhood, one of children has gone to live there. They have come for a month and stayed. It's true everyone speaks English, but *það er gott að læra tungumálið*, it is good to learn the language. The conversion of the Icelanders to Christianity occurred in the year 999 and was notable for its rapidity. All Icelanders would convert, ruled Thorgeir Thorkelsson, but pagans would be allowed to worship the old gods in secret. Among the inducements for converting, trade with other nations ranked high, so perhaps the conversion was not as whole-hearted as it appeared. But then the pagan ways soon fell into the realm of pre-history, that sphere whose job it is to reassure modern nations how far they have come. If you wish to stand by the waterfall and pray to Odin now there is nothing to stop you. And do you think much about the old country, someone will ask my child. I think of it as a kind of prehistory, showing how far we have come. They will drop references to the old country casually in conversation, to the point where they will wonder why, if it plays so much on their mind, they ever left. Then they will understand that its role is to be that place framed by leaving, for unpacking to others who have not lived there and find an interest in tales of the country, unimaginable to its mere inhabitants. The wind carries Anna Þorvaldsdóttir's *Aeriality*, with the shifting currents of its great soundclouds and its plumes of microtonality rising over the orchestra, parting to reveal an Icelandic stormbeach, here where the North Sea washes against the skirt of a volcano, its head lost in clouds. I watch an Icelandic crime drama and notice how the characters signal to one another, from whatever distance, from the windows of their houses huddled round the harbour of their far-northern town, whether by hand, by candle or torch. All in their different ways are watching and waiting, as the northernness allows itself to unfold. There is something it knows and wishes to tell us. But I am long dead and this revelation is not for me.

§ 98

To make an end of all my talk of compass points, I realise now it was always east, and not just east, but east-the-better-to-travel-west. I began by the sea in the east, from whence I retreated into the mountains. Travelling east across the sea I found the sea again, only to find myself pushed back west as the land fell away from under my feet. Travelling to my third east I once more fled inland from the sea to the mountains. There is I now realise a religious aspect to the quest I have mapped out here, without my being remotely religious then or now. I found a village at the end of an isthmus whose stained-glass window initiated this journey. In my second east I found a social-realist world where the illuminations of religion had shrunk to a few stained-glass panes in a pub window. In my third east I found a different picture again. It was not a noticeably Catholic region; in fact its Catholic population was among the smallest in the country. But before the Jacobite risings its Catholic population had been the highest in Scotland. As this pattern dissolved in the eighteenth century, it was replaced by an Episcopalian, or high-church Anglican element, which resulted in a notably different picture from the familiar Catholic-Protestant stand-offs of the west of the country. Going in search of Catholic relics, I find myself back in the mountains, the westerly terminus of my rebound from the east. Here Gaelic survived latest, here the valleys are longest and highest and coldest, here the old religion lingered too. In a poem I find a chapel named Our Lady of the Snows. Is it real: yes it is. Some ingenuity is required to locate it. Nearby is Corgarff castle, burned by the rebels in the first Jacobite Rising when its laird took the government side, burned by the government in the second when he came out for the rebels. Driving to it in deep December down a track I notice another car coming and pulling over notice it is, of all people, the queen. Further down the road is a hunting lodge she had given her son and daughter-in-law on their wedding. The gift had not gone well and the lodge fell into disuse. Even in her nineties, however, the monarch likes to keep up old ways, and remains a keen shooter, letting off her arquebuse at any game birds in sight, whose necks she has been known to wring herself. In pulling in I offer her the customary raised index finger, and would rather not say if she reciprocates in kind. And just over there down another track is the chapel. In a farmyard. Unlocked. Not recently visited. Used/disused status: indeterminate. And a stained-glass window. In three panels. A background of hills, fields and rivers. Then a shamrock inlaid in a cross of St John. Kaleidoscope lines of blue and white in the cross reminding me of sheets of interlocked ice on the Dee or Don or a mountain loch. Turning in on itself to that improbable waterborne bloom in the heart of the ice and lit for me now by the low midwinter sun. There is the glass and beyond it nothing. Here at the end, with the whole world left behind over my shoulder, lost now and fading to black.

§ 99

I'm close . . . I'm down . . . face in the snow . . . swimming in bilge . . . director, some music . . . spiky for preference . . . keep going, I thought . . . something will happen . . . you'll know when you see it . . . clutching your coat round you . . . all buttons gone . . . follow the light source . . . somewhere behind glass . . . that dark too bright . . . in and through . . . from one world to another . . . through is back . . . that's the idea . . . like weaving the dark . . . that stitch repeated . . . Hamish is here . . . he'll help you, I thought . . . hisses and spits . . . brutish ingrate . . . what's in his head . . . pass through the dark and find it . . . much like here . . . and again . . . I'm close . . . it's coming . . . one more effort . . . here in the mountains . . . enough of your day-trips and . . . garden centres . . . what are you, some kind of . . . Sunday driver . . . lift your eyes to the low sun . . . they see it in their far-flung . . . bungalows and estates . . . pulling into their . . . motorway services . . . what are they waiting for . . . the child has been sick in the car . . . all too much for him . . . give him an orange and press on . . . he'll thank you for it . . . I remember the troughs . . . between mountains . . . the sea was a trough . . . on the way . . . the ferry bobbed on the tide . . . and I knew we were climbing . . . all that time . . . as I see it from here . . . what were they thinking . . . the others . . . the lorry drivers . . . queuing for fry-ups . . . not knowing . . . that we were climbing already . . . I felt it . . . it's close, I told them . . . could have told them . . . my method, was there a method . . . merely a kind of . . . demented repetition . . . wear down the resistance . . . I'm close, I say . . . I'm down and back up . . . can't stop me, can't stop myself . . . I knew the way all along . . .

when I walked the long flat streets . . . what was I waiting for . . . biding my time . . . it's coming . . . Hamish . . . blood on the snow . . . feathers and screams . . . I've wanted it . . . open your eyes . . . in the dark . . . a feeling of entering . . . stained glass . . . the colours slowing down . . . to a stop . . . no, not yet . . . am I repeating myself . . . and how many others . . . I've changed . . . not enough . . . there's still time . . . so many mistakes . . . but the right ones . . . to get here . . . director, some music . . . I can't hear it . . . the mud in my ears . . . on all fours in the quag . . . then up ahead . . . a chapel . . . you'll be happy with that, I thought . . . eyes opening now . . . as though after long sleep . . . is it possible . . . to sleep on the move . . . crossing the sea . . . down the motorway . . . in the slipstream of all those . . . huge hulking lorries . . . what was I thinking . . . no, even then I . . . knew I was close . . . it's not much further, I said . . . who has come with me . . . this time . . . are you still here . . . Hamish . . . mouthful of snow . . . follow me . . . weaving that dark . . . crawling over my grave . . . hold me . . . don't let go . . . we're going in . . . and through . . . so many mistakes . . . all the right ones . . . to have got here at all . . . coat flapping . . . gripping the snow . . . hang on . . . I'm getting ahead of you . . . but we're close . . . say we've arrived . . . or nearly . . . I'm waiting . . . help me . . . where has your hand gone . . . one last time . . . keep going . . . I feel it . . . my breath on the snow . . .

§ 100

Who am I now,
Leschangie hill, in
the shifting mirror of
memory: father or child?
I fell behind on the forest path
to frame us at large among pines
and spruce, and seeing you wander
thought of reciting something –
Russian for preference –
'our path was through forget-
me-nots and wild dog roses,
I wore no coat, words clung
like leaves to the trees . . .' –
following where a village doctor
might traipse over fields to treat
a consumptive or a soldier home
from the wars. Sodden
beneath shrugging conifers
I stumbled on a tree root
where we stopped to read
A Midsummer Night's Dream
and feast on berries
(it is a pleasure to fall down
with an attractive woman) –
wild berries, their over-ripe joy
clasped in a baby's hand
to burst against the palate
in blood-red streams. Over

the hill lay the sunken mill-
pond and tumbledown
bothy – domino sets
of tadpoles spilled on the large
flat stones under the algae,
half-sunk cement bags
agape in the breeze, and
a tractor tyre drowned in its lining.
Already day was burning
up the horizon along
the line where clouds and hay-
ricks met and a barn in a far
field was a furnace reflected;
then coming down the other
side we moved into shadow and
reached the old factory where
a cat colony ate from sauce-pans –
a three-legged black cat
darting over the hot stones
like a dropped glove
carried off in a breeze.
I peered through a window
and saw cascades of indoor
rain on abandoned post
and where the plaster had fallen
in lumps, outdoors trying
to get in and indoors trying
to get out, before we sat in
an overgrown windowless
fire-engine and felt fresh moss
at our feet. Already awash,
the zone was an overflow
of prodigal roots, burns,

buds and berries. Yet even
now I felt already home and
feeding the scene through
the mirror, watching the ceiling
under the sky come down
and with it a plashy drenching:
the children scooped in our
arms and off up the hill
while I reeled in the mill-pond,
the buzzards and harebells
tucked now into a rucksack
pocket. The glassy white discs
are honesty, the snowberries
fit just so between a fleeing
child's finger and thumb,
their palms more daring and
lighter than birds. Sodden,
she too, the children's mother
shakes out her hair through
the raindrop lens of my gaze,
too much immediacy wiped
away like the downpour from
my eyes, and the laughter
among the trees still coming
after us down the path,
following what can only
have been the right way home.

Our child begins to dance and wave their arms about while emitting a strange chirping song. It is Grieg's *In the Hall of the Mountain King*. The piece opens by ascending a minor scale from B to F#, descending to F natural and E, then climbing again to a major scale running from D to A. This motif is repeated eighteen times. I know this from the innumerable times our child has pressed repeat on the stereo to listen to it over and over for hours on end, and from the exactly eighteen repetitions of the motif our child performs now. Not in accompaniment of the stereo any longer, since that has now been turned off while our child internalises the music, much as a spider might 'internalise' a fly caught in their web. When the child dances close to me I become aware of a teeth-grinding action that accompanies the dance, a sucking and pulling tight that might even be quite painful. Here comes the end of the piece though, its crashing chords like a thunderstorm to send us scampering for cover. A yellow conductor's baton is deployed enthusiastically. Arms are flailed and in their excitement our child falls over, hardly noticing, before beginning again. As the piece repeats I am aware that the singing has become fainter, and the identity of the piece may no longer be so obvious to an observer. By now it is less a performance than an interpretation. Our child is highly musical and will often play the instruments in the house, though not in any conventional way. They might play a piano piece with their bottom, or lie down beside a violin and stroke it, gently, for quite some time. Or they might go one step further and play a Bach toccata and fugue on an invisible organ in their bedroom. Though exposed to a lot of music and expressing strong musical preferences, our child will often insist we turn the stereo off or sit in silence in the car. The ensuing silences are then typically filled by these interior replays of current favourite pieces such as the Grieg. Would you like to see them do *In the Hall of the Mountain King*, I imagine asking the child's grandparents. Will he be playing it on the piano, or singing along? He will be lying on the sofa, twitching his baton occasionally and grinding his teeth. Pythagoras believed – this again – that the planets emit a humming sound derived from their revolutions round the sun, on a level inaudible to the human ear: the music of the spheres. Refining these theories, Kepler expounded his own theories not just of cosmogony but harmony and tuning. And while my attempts to listen in to the music of the spheres resonating inwardly, in the soul, as Kepler believed, have thus far come to naught, many people are happy to think of outer space as being full of very loud noises, as in science fiction films, when spaceships explode. But in closing I note that sounds cannot occur in a vacuum, and if our planet were to explode it would do so, from the perspective of a far-off observer, not us – we being no longer required in this scenario – in silence.

Vectors

1 Angela Griffith, Marguerite Helmers and Róisín Kennedy (eds), *Harry Clarke and Artistic Visions of the New Irish State* (Irish Academic Press, 2018).

2 John Keats, *Lamia, Isabella, The Eve of St Agnes, and Other Poems* (1820).

3 James Clarence Mangan, 'An Extraordinary Adventure in the Shades' (*Comet* 20–27 January 1833).

4 Michel Butor, *La modification* (Éditions de Minuit, 1957).

5 Rebecca Tamás, 'Joan of Arc', in *Savage* (Clinic, 2017).

6 Somhairle MacGhill-Eathain and Robert Garioch, *Seventeen Poems for 6d* (Chalmers Press, 1940).

7 Theodor W. Adorno, 'Bach Defended Against His Devotees', in *Prisms* (trs Samuel and Shierry Weber, MIT Press, 1982).

8 Freda Laughton, 'The Welcome', in *A Transitory House* (Jonathan Cape, 1945).

9 Barbara Guest, 'Roses', in *Moscow Mansions* (Viking, 1973).

10 Jana Prikryl, 'Vertical', in *No Matter* (Tim Duggan Books, 2019).

11 Thomas Kinsella, 'Hen Woman', in *New Poems* (Oxford, 1973).

12 Dónall MacAmhlaigh, *Dialann Deoraí* (An Clóchomhar, 1960).

13 Peter Didsbury, *A Fire Shared* (LegalHighsPress, 2020).

14 Aimé Césaire, *Cahier d'un retour au pays natal* (Volontés, 1939).

15 Kathleen Jamie, 'The Tay Moses', in *Jizzen* (Picador, 1999).

16 Jorge Luis Borges, 'La biblioteca be Babel' in *El Jardin de senderos que se bifurcan* (Editorial Sur, 1941).

17 Davey Graham, *After Hours at Hull University 4th February 1967* (Rollercoaster, 2012).

18 Helen Macdonald, *Shaler's Fish* (Etruscan Books, 2002).

19 H. D., *Helen in Egypt* (New Directions, 1961).

20 Roy Fisher, *The Cut Pages* (Fulcrum Press, 1971).

21 Mervyn Morris, 'Literary Evening, Jamaica', in *The Pond: A Book of Poems* (New Beacon Books, 1973).

22 Andrei Tarkovsky, *Solaris* (1972).

23 Carol Rumens, 'Thinking About Montale by the River Hull', in *Blind Spots* (Seren, 2008).

24 Sally M. Foster, *Picts, Gaels and Scots: Early Historic Scotland* (Birlinn, 2014).

25 Medbh McGuckian, 'On Not Being Your Lover', in *Venus and the Rain* (Oxford, 1984).

26 Hull City 1 (Geovanni), Liverpool FC 3 (Alonso, Kuyt (2)), KC Stadium, 25 April 2009.

27 Deòrsa Caimbeul Hay, *Mochtàr is Dùghall* (Roinn nan Cànan Ceilteach, 1982) .

28 Valzhyna Mort, 'Nocturne for a Moving Train', in *Music for the Dead and Resurrected: Poems* (Farrar, Straus and Giroux, 2020).

29 David Wheatley, *Dark and True and Tender* (CB Editions, 2012).

30 Máirín Nic Eoin, *B'ait Leo Bean* (An Clóchomhar, 1998).

31 Lord William Percy, *Three Studies in Bird Character: Bitterns, Herons and Water Rails* (Country Life, 1951).

32 Allen Curnow, 'Investigations at the Public Baths', in *The Bells of St Babel's* (Carcanet, 2002).

33 Darach Ó Catháin, *Traditional Irish Unaccompanied Singing* (Gael-Linn, 1994).

34 Marianne Moore, 'Marriage', in *Observations: Poems* (Dial Press, 1924).

35 Bohumil Hrabal, *Too Loud a Solitude* (tr. Michael Henry Heim, Abacus, 1993).

36 Fairport Convention, 'Farewell, Farwell', from *Liege and Lief* (Island, 1969).

37 Lewis Grassic Gibbon, *Sunset Song* (Jarrolds, 1932).

38 Ted Lewis, *Jack's Return Home* (Michael Joseph, 1970).

39 Barry McCrea, *Languages of the Night: Minor Languages and the Literary Imagination in Twentieth-Century Ireland and Europe* (Yale University Press, 2015).

40 Peter Davidson, *Distance and Memory* (Carcanet, 2013).

41 Sir Andrew Leith Hay, *Castles of Aberdeenshire: Historical and Descriptive Notices* (1887).

42 Ali Smith, *Hotel World* (Hamish Hamilton, 2001).

43 Rebecca Solnit, *Wanderlust: A History of Walking* (Penguin, 2001).

44 Rosemary Tonks, 'The Drinkers of Coffee', in *Iliad of Broken Sentences* (Bodley Head, 1967).

45 Arnold Schoenberg, *Fundamentals of Musical Composition* (Faber and Faber, 1967).

46 Cornelius Cardew, *Stockhausen Serves Imperialism* (Latimer New Directions, 1974)

47 Gaston Bachelard, *La poétique de l'espace* (Presses Universitaire de France, 1957).

48 Conor O'Callaghan, *Nothing On Earth* (Doubleday, 2016).

49 Séamus Dall Mac Cuarta, 'Fáilte don Éan', in Thomas Kinsella and Seán Ó Tuama (eds), *An Duanaire, 1600–1900: Poems of the Dispossessed* (Dolmen, 1981).

50 George Oppen, 'Exodus', in *Seascape: Needle's Eye* (1972).

51 Ellis O'Connor, *West #3*, oil on canvas, author's collection.

52 Kirsty Gunn, *The Big Music* (Faber and Faber, 2012).

53 Robert Louis Stevenson, *Kidnapped* (1886).

54 Ludwig Wittgenstein, *Philosophical Investigations* (Macmillan, 1953).

55 Ian Hamilton Finlay, 'Advertising Fascism' ('Published by Committee of Public Safety', Little Sparta, 1987).

56 Robert Pinget, *L'inquisitoire* (Éditions de Minuit, 1962).

57 Gerald Murnane, personal communication to the author, 18 September 2020.

58 Luigi Nono, *Lontananza Utopica Nostalgia Futura* (1988).

59 Georges Perec, *Un homme qui dort* (Denoël, 1967).

60 J. H. Prynne, 'If There is a Stationmaster at Stamford S. D. Hardly So', in *The White Stones* (1969, Grosseteste Press).

61 Unpublished statement on poetics by Larry Eigner typed on the back of an envelope, postmarked 22 July 1987.

62 Nan Shepherd, *The Living Mountain* (Aberdeen University Press, 1977).

63 Joni Mitchell, *Blue* (Reprise, 1971).

64 Jen Hadfield, *Nigh-No-Place* (Bloodaxe, 2008).

65 Jane Stevenson and Peter Davidson (eds), *Early Modern Women*

Poets: An Anthology (Oxford UP, 2001).

66 Robert Musil, *Der Mann Ohne Eigenschaften* (1930–1943).

67 Muriel Rukeyser, *The Speed of Darkness* (Random House, 1968).

68 Lorine Niedecker, 'For Paul', in *My Life by Water: Collected Poems 1936–1968* (Fulcrum Press, 1970).

69 Sir Thomas Browne, *Hydrotaphia, Urn Burial, or, A Discourse of the Sepulchral Urns lately found in Norfolk* (1658).

70 Federico García Lorca, *El Paseo de Buster Keaton* (1925).

71 Joanne Limburg, *The Autistic Alice* (Bloodaxe, 2017).

72 Anna Kavan, *Ice* (Peter Owen, 1967).

73 Eiléan Ní Chuilleanáin, 'The Nave', in *The Sunfish* (Gallery Press, 2009).

74 Tabitha Lasley, *Sea State* (Fourth Estate, 2021).

75 F. Fraser Darling, *A Naturalist on Rona: Essays of a Biologist in Isolation* (Clarendon Press, 1939).

76 Rachael Boast, 'Moment in a labyrinth of moving images (after Alain Resnais), in *Hotel Raphael* (Picador, 2021).

77 Henri Michaux, *La nuit remue* (Gallimard, 1957).

78 Calum Kennedy, *The King of the Highlands* (Legacy Recordings, 2004)

79 Theodor W. Adorno, *Minima Moralia* (Verso, 1978).

80 Denise Riley, *Time Lived, Without Its Flow* (Capsule Editions, 2012).

81 J. B. Malone, *The Complete Wicklow Way: A Step-by-Step Guide* (O'Brien Press, 1988).

82 Anna Mendelssohn, *Implacable Art* (Equipage, 2000).

83 Lucy Brock-Broido, 'Elective Mutes', in *A Hunger* (Random House, 2005).

84 Veronica Forrest-Thomson, *Poetic Artifice* (Manchester University Press, 1978).

85 John Coltrane, *Ascension* (Impulse, 1966).

86 Ian Crockatt (tr.), *Crimsoning the Eagle's Claw: The Viking Poems of Rognvaldr Kali Kolsson Earl of Orkney* (Arc Publications, 2014).

87 Ann Quin, *Berg* (Calder & Boyars, 1964)

88 György Ligeti, *Atmosphères* (1961).

89 Ishion Hutchinson, 'Train to Cambridge' (personal communication to the author, April 2021).

90 Louis Wolfson, *Le schizo et les langues* (Gallimard, 1970).

91 Walter Benjamin, 'The Railway Disaster at the Firth of Tay', radio talk broadcast by Berliner Funkstunde, February 1932.

92 Michael Davidson, 'Disability Poetics', in Cary Nelson (ed.), *The Oxford Handbook of Modern and Contemporary American Poetry* (Oxford University Press, 2012).

93 Rose Macaulay, *Pleasure of Ruins* (Thames & Hudson, 1953).

94 Rebecca Elson, *A Responsibility to Awe* (Oxford Poets, 2001).

95 Denise Levertov, 'The Ache of Marriage', in *O Taste and See* (New Directions, 1964).

96 Christine Brooke-Rose, *Life, End Of* (Carcanet, 2006).

97 Anna Þorvaldsdóttir, *Aeriality* (2011).

98 Postcard collected from summit of Morven, Aberdeenshire.

99 Samuel Beckett, *Cascando and Other Short Dramatic Pieces* (Grove Press, 1968).

100 Andrei Tarkovsky, *Mirror* (1975).

101 Edward Grieg, *In the Hall of the Mountain King* (1875), performance by child of author.